"Dr. Tanner's *Health Care Innovation* is a highly readable guide to innovation. He draws on his DuPont experiences, and other sources, to explain how the spark of creativity can create unexpected value. He demonstrates that innovation is not just a science — it can occur in all human endeavor."

Thomas Connelly, Executive Vice President
and Chief Innovation Officer, DuPont Company

"In a rapidly transforming healthcare environment, quality healthcare professionals are embracing and adding innovative thinking strategies and techniques to their toolkits. In *Health Care Innovation*, Dr. Tanner provides quality healthcare professionals a practical framework for guiding their teams through the innovative problem solving process."

Stacy Sochacki, Executive Director,
National Association for Healthcare Quality

"Dr. Tanner's new book, *Health Care Innovation*, describes innovation strategies, concepts and techniques in a clear, succinct and easy to grasp manner. The book provides an effective blueprint for healthcare professionals to equip themselves with the necessary innovation skills to energize their teams. The industrial and healthcare examples Dr. Tanner uses throughout his book are realistic, attainable and motivational."

L. Dale Harvey, MS, RN, Patient Safety Fellow, Director,
Performance Improvement, VCU Health System and National
Association for Healthcare Quality Innovations Team Leader

HEALTH CARE INNOVATION

Empowered by Innovative Thinking

David Tanner

Includes stories about health care innovations reported by AHRQ's Health Care Innovations Exchange as well as industry innovations — from Kevlar® to crawfish bait.

Health Care Innovation Empowered by Innovative Thinking

For information on permissions or to purchase multiple copies at volume discounts, contact the publisher:

Rockville Institute
1600 Research Boulevard
Rockville, MD 20850-3129

The Agency for Healthcare Research and Quality, Health Care Innovations Exchange gave permission to use health care innovations that were reported on its web site.

Frank and Ernest cartoons in the book are used by permission of Tom Thaves on behalf of his father, Bob Thaves.

Edited by Russ Mardon, PhD, Senior Study Director, Westat.

Cover illustration and inside graphic design by Linda Beatty, Westat.

ISBN Number-13: 978-0-9837127-0-1

Dedication

To all innovators and health care organizations
striving to enhance health care innovation

Acknowledgments

I am grateful to the following people:

Veronica Nieva, Westat, Project Director for the Agency for Healthcare Research and Quality (AHRQ), Health Care Innovations Exchange, and Deborah Carpenter, Project Manager for the AHRQ Health Care Innovations Exchange, for their strong support and encouragement to write and publish this book.

Russ Mardon, Senior Study Director, Westat and Editorial Task Leader of AHRQ Health Care Innovations Exchange biweekly web site. Russ did a very thorough and professional job in editing the book, which upgraded readability and value.

Linda Beatty, Westat, who did a very professional job in design of the book cover and internal book pages. Laura Milcetich, Westat, who kindly provided me with useful references and material derived from the Innovations Exchange. Evarilla Cover, Westat, who conducted a careful review and edit of the manuscript.

Mary Nix, Project Officer for AHRQ, who recommended that I be invited to become an "expert panel" member of AHRQ Health Care Innovations Exchange.

Edward de Bono, Ned Herrmann, and Michael Kirton, whose lectures and workshops stimulated me to learn and introduce creative thinking techniques into the DuPont Company.

The American Creativity Association, whose purpose is to promote a more creative society, motivated me to stay active in the field of creativity and innovation after retirement from the DuPont Company.

Tom Thaves for kindly giving permission to use the *Frank and Ernest* cartoons in this book.

Stan Gryskiewicz for kindly giving permission to include the section describing a jazz musician's perspective about innovative teams.

My wife, Lee Tanner, who constructively critiqued each chapter in this book.

Contents

Chapter 1

Introduction

The objective of this book is to communicate knowledge about creativity and innovation drawn from the industrial sector to innovators and organizations in the health care sector. As noted in the Institute of Medicine's *Crossing the Quality Chasm*, a number of well-understood design principles drawn from other industries, as well as today's health care organizations, could help greatly in improving the care that is provided to patients. By drawing on my personal experience managing the innovation process in industry, and illustrating these ideas with real-world health care challenges and innovative solutions, this book can help make these necessary connections.

My motivation to write this book stemmed from a meeting I attended on May 4, 2010 as a new panel member of the Agency for Healthcare Research and Quality (AHRQ), Health Care Innovations Exchange. This government agency administers a free, publicly available web site, updated biweekly, dedicated to providing information about health care innovations focused on patient care, and promoting their uptake and adoption. It includes innovative programs in a wide variety of settings including hospitals, nursing homes, community clinics, schools, prisons, and homes. The site focuses on the new approaches to the delivery of health care services rather than on technological or therapeutic innovations. The web site (www.innovations.ahrq.gov) includes descriptions of more than 500 health care innovations as of November 2010 and has more than 100,000 visits per month and more than 40,000 subscribers.

Two health care innovation stories related at the meeting were particularly inspiring. The first was told by Dr. Bruce Leff of the Johns Hopkins Bayview Medical Center and involved the *Hospital at Home* innovation. The other was told by Steve Shields, President and CEO, Meadowlark Hills, about the creation of the *Households Program in Nursing Home* innovation.

This book covers the following topics:

- Sources of innovation
- The role of the innovator
- Innovator characteristics
- Innovative problem solving
- Innovative thinking tools and applications
- The value of diversity in thinking
- Promoting a supportive environment

At the end of each chapter are three health care innovation stories pertinent to the contents of that chapter.

Each health care innovation is listed in the References section of the book with information about how to locate the innovation in the Innovations Exchange web site, where it is described in much greater detail. The web site also includes the name of the innovator and how that person can be reached for more information about the innovation and its status.

Many industrial innovation stories are integrated throughout the book, particularly in Chapter 5, *Innovative Thinking Techniques*, and Chapter 7, *Promoting an Innovative Culture*. Chapter 3, *Role of the Innovator*, includes the inside story of the Kevlar® innovation.

Innovative thinking in the context of this book is synonymous with creative thinking and the two terms are occasionally used interchangeably. Some portions of this book were drawn from the author's previous two books.[1, 2]

The Internet Phrase Finder (www.phrases.org.uk) makes the point that nothing defines a culture as clearly as its language, and the element of language that best encapsulates a society's values and beliefs is its proverbs. Throughout the book, a variety of non-biblical proverbs are cited that communicate timeless wisdoms and express some traditionally held truths about topics discussed.

I hope that this book will be of value to health care innovators and organizations striving to bring new patient health care innovations to reality.

Chapter 2

Sources of Innovation

All innovations are either discovery-driven or needs-driven.

Discovery-Driven Innovation

Discovery-driven innovation occurs when a fortuitous accident or unexpected event is observed leading to an invention that an observant innovator might formulate into a new innovation. There are many examples including Alexander Fleming's invention of penicillin, Alfred Nobel's invention of dynamite, and Roy Plunkett's invention of "Teflon."

The following cartoon exemplifies discovery-driven innovation:

Serendipity

Reprinted with permission. Frank and Ernest Cartoons ©Thaves.

Needs-Driven Innovation

Needs-driven innovation occurs when an important need is identified, innovators generate innovative ideas to meet the need, and take the best idea to reality.

This cartoon exemplifies needs-driven innovation:

Needs-Driven Innovation

Reprinted with permission. Frank and Ernest Cartoons ©Thaves.

Both sources of innovation are important. Both are influenced by an innovative culture that supports the environment for innovative thinking and innovation. But needs-driven innovation is more controllable. Most, if not all, industrial and health care innovations are triggered by a need recognized by an innovator or an organization that takes steps to generate ideas to meet the need. The focus of this book is needs-driven innovation.

Everyone is familiar with this well-known proverb pertinent to needs-driven innovation:

Necessity is the mother of invention.

This proverb is based on the line "Necessity, who is the mother of invention" in *The Republic*, written by the Greek author and philosopher Plato, (427-347 BC), and remains a vital insight today. Although not all situations require emergency actions, the current dynamic health care reform environment, coupled with our global and domestic economic challenges, create serious situations that need action-oriented innovative solutions. Innovators play a vital role in championing these needs-driven solutions.

The "Honey Pot" Story

A good example of needs-driven innovation in industry is the "Honey Pot" story, told by Dr. Edward Glassman, former head of the program for team effectiveness, Department of Biochemistry and Nutrition, School of Medicine, Chapel Hill, NC.

The story begins with a description of a need to solve a problem and stresses the value of bringing together a group of people with diverse backgrounds to generate ideas for possible solutions. It also illustrates that no idea is too crazy or too wild.

An electric utility faced a significant problem every time there was an ice storm. Ice would collect on power lines, and they would break under the weight. The company's solution to this problem was to send line workers to climb the pole and shake the wires. However, this was an undesirable task because the time when the activity was needed was also the least desirable time to climb the poles. It was cold, damp, and icy.

The utility gathered people with a variety of backgrounds to "brainstorm" solutions to the problem. During a break, the moderator heard a conversation between two line workers: "I hate this job. I sure hope we come up with a better way to get the ice off the lines. Last week, in addition to almost falling off the pole, I was chased by a big brown bear for about two miles. He just wouldn't give up."

Upon reconvening, the moderator retold the story. One participant said, "The answer is obvious. We need to train the bears to climb the poles and shake the wires." Everybody laughed. Then another said, "The bears wouldn't have to shake the wires. They are so heavy that their weight on the end of the pole would be sufficient to shake the ice off." The group laughed again. "It's impossible to train the bears to climb the pole," someone said. "Well, then, we just have to make it natural for the bears to climb the pole. We'll put honey pots on top of the poles. The bears will climb the poles to get the honey and knock the ice off at the same time," said another. "But, then, they'll just get the honey in clear weather and not climb the poles when it's icy," another answered.

And to that someone said, "That's an easy problem to solve. You know all those helicopters the company just bought to shuttle executives around? Well, they'll just have to walk when it's icy. We'll fly the copters around, putting the honey pots on top of the poles after an ice storm, the bears will climb the poles, and the ice will be shaken off."

Then one participant spoke for the first time, "My husband used to be a chopper pilot in Vietnam, and he told me that the downdraft from these choppers is really something. If we just flew the choppers over the icy power lines, the downdraft should knock the ice off. No men; no bears; no honey pots—just the downdraft from the helicopters." As you might guess, her idea worked and that's how the company removed ice from power lines.

Renowned Innovators

In 1974, Peter Drucker, a well-known innovative thinker, commented on the need for companies and their management to pursue innovation:

> An established company that in an age demanding innovation is not capable of innovation is doomed to decline and extinction. And a management, that in such a period does not know how to manage innovation, is incompetent and unequal to its task.

Drucker took steps to meet this need by writing many books on the topic of innovation such as *Innovation and Entrepreneurship*.[3]

Alex Osborn recognized the need for a group problem solving technique in which all members of the group could participate. This innovative thinking led to the well-known process of *brainstorming*.[4] Osborn also recognized the need for a process to solve problems in a systematic way and fathered the creative problem solving process described in his book, *Applied Imagination*.[4]

Edward de Bono, in his book *The Mechanism of Mind*,[5] recognized the need to develop creative thinking tools to help people step outside their normal thinking patterns in dealing with difficult problems and searching for new opportunities.[5] Hence he developed *lateral thinking* and many other creative thinking tools.[6] He also recognized the need for a focused-thinking process, which led to the *Six Thinking Hats* framework.[7] Lateral thinking and the Six Thinking Hats are discussed in Chapter 5.

Ned Herrmann recognized the need to integrate the scientific study of the brain with the study of the development of human creativity. To meet this need, he invented the *Herrmann Brain Dominance Instrument*® (HBDI®). The basic concept of the Herrmann® model is a metaphor for the brain composed of four interactive quadrants, each representing a category of thinking preferences.[8, 9] Combined together, these four quadrants represent the Whole Brain® Thinking Model. It is discussed in Chapter 6.

Michael Kirton recognized the need for an instrument that measures people's creativity styles. To meet this need, he developed the widely applied *Kirton Adaption-Innovation Inventory* (KAI).* The KAI is described in numerous journal articles, theses, and his book *Adapters and Innovators: Styles of Creativity and Problem Solving*.[10] It is discussed in Chapter 6.

---

* The Kirton Adaption-Innovation Inventory (KAI), KAI, and KAI Inventory are used with the permission of Dr. M. J. Kirton.

Health Care Innovations

The following pages describe three health care innovations that exemplify needs-driven innovation.

Aiding Teens With Chronic Asthma[11]

Summary of the Program

The San Mateo Medical Center distributed mobile phones with customized disease management software to young asthma patients, enabling them to communicate with and receive real-time feedback from providers on at least a daily basis. The communication focused on how to better manage asthma on an ongoing basis, with the goal of reducing triggers that might lead to costly acute episodes. The initiative enhanced compliance with the daily diary and with medication regimens, which in turn led to better patient outcomes, less use of rescue medications, and fewer emergency department (ED) visits and missed school days.

The Need

San Mateo Medical Center cares for more than 1,000 children and teenagers with severe persistent asthma, most of whom live in poverty and are bilingual. Historically, these patients received uncoordinated care with little between-visit monitoring, causing high use of the ED and clinics when symptoms were exacerbated.

Innovative leaders at San Mateo recognized a need to improve care for asthma patients and reduce unscheduled physician visits, ED use, and hospitalizations by identifying new ways to engage patients outside the clinic. San Mateo's clinicians, moreover, believed that having regular access to patient-reported data was the key to effective monitoring and their ability to provide focused, timely interventions to prevent acute exacerbations.

The Needs-Driven Innovation

The California HealthCare Foundation alerted San Mateo leaders to the BeWell Mobile Technology system and provided a grant that enabled San Mateo to purchase the application and to fund cell phone service and the salary of an asthma care coordinator. San Mateo Medical Center distributed mobile phones with customized disease-management software to young asthma patients, enabling them to communicate with and receive real-time feedback from providers on at least a daily basis. The communication focuses on how to better manage asthma on an ongoing basis, with the goal of reducing triggers that might lead to costly acute episodes.

Results

An 8-month pilot test conducted at the San Mateo Medical Center found that this innovative initiative enhanced compliance with the daily diary and with medication regimens, which in turn led to better patient outcomes, less use of rescue medications, and fewer ED visits and missed school days.

Use by Other Organizations

Kaiser Permanente has implemented a BeWell Mobile Diabetes Assistant application with 84 adults diagnosed with type 1 or type 2 diabetes and poor glycemic control. Results show meaningful improvements in blood glucose levels.

The University of California at San Francisco and Kaiser Permanente Division of Research have also each used the BeWell Mobile platform and diary applications for patient-recorded outcomes in primary research.

Support for Breast Cancer Patients[13]

Summary of the Program

The University of California San Francisco Breast Care Center Decision Services unit offers a consultation planning, recording, and summarizing service in which trained interns help patients brainstorm and write down a list of questions and concerns for their providers, accompany patients to their medical appointments to audio record and take notes, and make sure all patient questions are addressed by the attending physician. The goal is to help the patient communicate more effectively with his or her physician and hence improve patient decision making. The program improved patient decision making and communication between provider and patient.

Specific program components (implemented at the University of California San Francisco and elsewhere) were found to be effective in increasing patient knowledge/recall and satisfaction, encouraging patients to ask more questions, and improving communication and decision making.

The Need

Many newly diagnosed breast cancer patients are often overwhelmed with their situation and do not know what questions to ask the doctor or how to use the information provided to make treatment decisions. There was a clear need to assist these patients in asking questions of their medical team and understanding how to use the information provided. Few programs offer such services.

The Needs-Driven Innovation

In 1994, Jeff Belkora analyzed data from a series of 23 focus groups with 250 breast cancer survivors conducted at the Palo Alto Community Breast Health Project. These sessions revealed a shared sense of confusion and anxiety about treatment options and decisions, stemming in large part from information overload and other barriers to patient-provider communication.

Dr. Belkora and colleagues conducted a needs assessment with patients that clearly indicated that they were not always able to express their priorities and preferences to clinicians in the context of a clinical consultation. This finding led to the idea of creating a consultation planning program to assist patients in preparing for their encounters through the use of a structured pre-consultation worksheet.

When patients schedule their medical visit, they are sent educational videos and offered the opportunity to be accompanied on their visit by a premedical intern. If the patient accepts this offer, a premedical intern and the patient meet one hour before the appointment in or near the exam room to prepare a list of questions for the doctor. If more convenient for the patient, the intern and patient meet by phone in the days before the appointment. During this consultation planning session, the intern uses a structured worksheet to help ensure that the patient's questions, concerns, and priorities are raised and discussed with the doctor. The intern does not provide any medical advice or clinical information during the consultation planning session.

Results

The program improved patient decision making and communication between provider and patient. Specific program components implemented at the University of California San Francisco were found to be effective in increasing patient knowledge/recall and satisfaction, encouraging patients to ask more questions, and improving communication and decision making.

Use by Other Organizations

The program is being pilot tested by The Cancer Support Community, a nationwide network of resource centers for people with cancer, and by the Edinburgh Cancer Centre in Scotland. Various components of the program have been adopted by resource centers in Northern California, including the Palo Alto Community Breast Health Project, the Cancer Resource Center of Mendocino County, and the Humboldt Community Breast Health Project. The Cancer Resource Center of Mendocino County has conducted the

Consultation Planning, Recording and Summarizing program in different forms for hundreds of patients facing various types of cancer, including breast, prostate, ovarian, colorectal, head and neck, and lung.

Criminal Justice Mental Health Court[13]

Summary of the Program

The Brooklyn Mental Health Court links eligible defendants to long-term treatment and monitoring of their mental health problems as an alternative to incarceration. The goal of these new model courts is to move beyond punishment to address the underlying problems that are leading to criminal behavior, thus reducing the chance of repeat offenses. Early evidence suggests that the program has been successful in generally reducing recidivism, homelessness, psychiatric hospitalizations, alcohol use, and substance abuse.

The Need

People with mental illness often do not fare well under the current criminal justice system, which can lead to the potential for repeat crimes. Because their underlying mental health problems are typically not addressed while incarcerated, people with mental illness often find themselves in a "revolving door" situation in which they commit crimes, serve their sentence, and then commit repeat offenses. Statistics show that individuals with mental health problems are disproportionately represented in U.S. jails and prisons. Thus, there was a clear need for mental health treatment for eligible defendants, coupled with judicial monitoring as an alternative to incarceration.

The Needs-Driven Innovation

A year-long study undertaken by the Center for Court Innovation, a public-private partnership sponsored by the New York State Unified Court System, examined the challenges faced by offenders with mental illness, current court-based approaches to overcoming these challenges, and areas of concern regarding mental health courts. The outcome of this study was the Brooklyn Mental Health Court innovation.

Planning for the Mental Health Court began in April 2001 and lasted for roughly a year. Key steps in the process included recruitment of a project director, a legal committee, the court judge, and a clinical director. It also involved finalizing eligibility criteria, treatment mandates, and cross training of mental health and criminal justice professionals.

The Brooklyn Mental Health Court offers mental health treatment to eligible defendants, coupled with judicial monitoring as an alternative to incarceration. Eligible defendants must have a "serious and persistent" mental illness for which there is a known treatment, such as schizophrenia, bipolar disorder, major depression, or schizoaffective disorder.

Individuals can be referred to the program through a variety of sources, including defense attorneys, the district attorney, and other judges. Several protocols were developed. All nonviolent felony and misdemeanor cases that are referred to the mental health court are evaluated for eligibility. In violent felony cases, the assistant district attorney has the right to "veto" this initial evaluation and prevent the case from going to the court.

For all cases that are referred for evaluation of eligibility, a thorough mental health assessment is conducted as a part of the determination of clinical eligibility for the program including psychosocial and psychiatric evaluation. Written summaries of each part of the evaluation are provided to the court judge, the prosecutor, and the defense attorney. To protect public safety, the court judge and the prosecutor each has the unilateral right to reject any case. Overall, roughly one-half of the individuals who are referred to the court for evaluation ultimately enroll as participants in the program.

As a condition of participation, all participants agree to plead guilty to the charges against them and to remain under court supervision for a specified period of time as an alternative to incarceration. During this time, participants are linked to community-based services based on individualized treatment plans that may include mental health treatment, substance abuse treatment, case management services, and housing support services.

All participants are monitored regularly by the court judge and a dedicated clinical team. During these sessions, the judge inquires about treatment progress and setbacks, family, and hobbies. Changes in the treatment plan are made as necessary to address problem areas such as noncompliance.

Individuals who successfully comply with their individualized treatment plans for the period they are under court supervision are eligible to "graduate" from the program. All charges against misdemeanor and nonviolent felony offenders are dropped. Felony charges for violent first-time offenders and repeat offenders are reduced to a misdemeanor. Those who do not complete the program are sentenced to a predetermined amount of time in jail or prison; 353 of the first 625 participants graduated, whereas 94 failed to graduate and were sentenced to jail time.

Results

Preliminary evidence suggests that the court has been successful in reducing recidivism, homelessness, psychiatric hospitalizations, and frequency and current use of alcohol and drugs. During the first few years of operation, the court handled roughly 45 cases per year. The volume is now up to 80 to 100 new participants per year. An outcome analysis of the first 37 participants found that the program has had a generally positive impact on outcomes.

Use by Other Organizations

The Council of State Governments Justice Center estimates that there were approximately 275 to 300 mental health courts in approximately 40 states as of early 2010, with more in the planning stages. There were 24 mental health courts in New York State.

Chapter 3

Role of the Innovator

An innovator, in the context of this book, is a person who brings a new idea or activity into practice to meet an important organizational need. Innovations succeed because of the drive, determination, and tenacity of innovators. This chapter describes the role and general characteristics of innovators.

Identifying a Need

The first step in needs-driven innovation occurs when the innovator, or organizational leadership, identifies a high-priority need. The next step is idea generation to meet that need. It's essential for the innovator to have a clear understanding of the need before undertaking steps to meet the need. Sometimes the innovator must dig deeper than what's on the surface, as illustrated in this parable (author unknown):

> Long ago in a distant land lived a baker of some distinction. He was considered by many to be the finest designer and decorator of cakes and pastries in the entire kingdom of Businessland. As it happened, the king of Businessland decided to hold a party for his fiftieth birthday and sent word to the baker to prepare for the celebration the largest and most wonderful birthday cake ever seen in the kingdom. The baker was delighted that the king had chosen him for such a high honor and immediately set out with great anticipation to design a magnificent masterpiece.

He immediately ordered twelve dozen eggs from the old woman who owned the chicken farm up the road, along with three sacks of sugar and twenty pounds of chocolate from the confectioner. When these arrived, he began mixing his cake. He measured out the sugar, added the eggs, and began to add the flour only to find that he did not have enough to make such a large cake. He ran down the street to the miller only to find that the miller had closed his shop and left town for the week to visit his mother in Wilmingham.

Fortunately for the baker, he was able to purchase more flour from the breadmaker, who charged him dearly since he knew how important this order was to the baker and that the miller was out of town. He prepared the rest of his batter and poured his handi-work into the molds that he had carefully handcrafted. He moved the molds over to his oven and to his great horror found that the molds for such a large and won-derful cake would not fit into the oven. He was greatly distressed, but did not despair for long. He found a large hammer and began smashing away at the oven. Within a few hours he had broken away the top of the oven and began the task of rebuilding the oven with a higher ceiling. Finally the oven was finished and he moved his precious molds into the oven. Soon the cake was finished and he moved the molds to his deco-rating area where he worked furiously to craft a cake of unparalleled beauty and awe

He rushed the cake over to the royal castle only to find that the celebration had already begun. Undaunted, he paraded the magnificent cake into the ballroom to the gasps and wonderment of the excited guests. To his absolute horror the king frowned, groaned, and announced angrily, "I hate chocolate!" The baker was thrown out of the castle and never heard from again.

This parable illustrates how an important needs-driven innovation can be fraught with unexpected outcomes, surprises, and setbacks. It punctuates the importance of the innovator understanding and defining the "core" need before undertaking a project.

Sometimes great things materialize from small needs-driven beginnings, as expressed in this proverb:

> *Mighty oaks from little acorns grow.*

This proverb was expressed in an essay by D. Everett in the *Columbia Orator*, 1797:

> *Large streams from little fountains flow,*
> *Tall oaks from little acorns grow.*

Little acorns don't always grow into mighty oaks, but innovator-driven health care innovation acorns, like the ones described throughout the book, often lead to a sequence of events that affects the personal lives, far and wide, of a great many people.

Innovator Characteristics

While people's thinking styles and behavior patterns differ, there are certain characteristics that most innovators have in common. Productive innovators generally embody some, if not all, of the seven important characteristics listed below and described in this section.

1. Discontent with the status quo
2. Open-minded
3. Positive thinking
4. Willing to take risks
5. Action-oriented
6. Persistent
7. Hard-working

1. Discontent with the Status Quo

Innovators have an absolute discontent with the status quo. They recognize important problems that affect organizational outcomes and take steps to change things. The AHRQ Health Care Innovations Exchange web site describes an ongoing stream of innovations, motivated by innovators' discontent with the status quo, who have taken needs-driven actions to improve health care current practices.

2. Open-Minded

Innovators seek alternative innovative solutions to meet an important need. They don't grab at the first idea but take time to search for alternatives. The innovative problem solving process described in Chapter 4 and the innovative thinking tools discussed in Chapter 5 will be helpful to health care innovators searching for alternative solutions to difficult problems.

3. Positive Thinking

Positive thinkers look forward, not backward. It is a state of mind that plays a vital role in driving forward new bottom-line innovations. Positive thinking often involves viewing a negative from different angles and turning it into a positive, as illustrated by the following story.

> Two shoe companies each sent a representative to a developing country to help decide whether to build a shoe factory. The first representative wired back—"Nobody wears shoes here; don't build factory." The second representative was an innovative thinker and wired back—"NOBODY WEARS SHOES HERE...OPPORTUNITY UNLIMITED...BUILD LARGE FACTORY!!"

4. *Willing to Take Risks*

Risk taking requires courage. People are often fearful of risk taking, which is perfectly normal. John McCain, in his book, *Why Courage Matters*, comments:

> …courage is not the absence of fear, but the capacity for action despite our fear.

Risk taking is the spirit fostering innovation. Innovators are willing to take risks when the needs-driven stake is high because they realize:

> *Nothing ventured, nothing gained.*

This proverb dates back to the 14th century and the French proverb: "He who never undertook anything never achieved anything." It refers to the wisdom that you can't get anywhere unless you are willing to take a risk.

Most successful innovators realize that risk taking doesn't need to be taking a "blind" chance. Risk taking can be a well thought-out course of action. A management challenge is to create an environment of trust, where failure is not punished, but rather used as a learning experience to aid future risk-taking successes.

5. *Action-Oriented*

Innovators motivated to accomplish a task realize that *action speaks louder than words*. What you do is more important than what you say. Often it's important for innovators to take rapid action because

> *A stitch in time saves nine.*

This proverb, recorded in 1732, exemplifies the idea that timely innovations can fix a problem before it becomes larger and harder to fix. Innovators realize the value of not procrastinating.

Alan Bean, former U.S. astronaut and respected adventurer, made the following statement during a Creativity Week meeting at the Center for Creative Leadership in Greensboro, NC:

> When you have a good idea, don't spend a lot of time talking about it or asking permission, just go out and do it!

6. Persistent

Successful innovators are persistent in pursuing their needs-driven innovations. Obstacles frequently arise, but the following proverb captures the attitude of most innovators:

> *If at first you don't succeed, try, try again.*

This proverb is traced back to several sources in the 18th century. It makes the point that persistence pays off. Don't let a first-time failure stop further attempts.

The comedian W. C. Fields is quoted as saying:

> If at first you don't succeed, try, try again. Then quit. There's no point in being a damn fool about it.

Innovators realize that, if the chance of success is high, only a fool would quit! They know when they have an important innovation to pursue and "champion" for it. If questioned, they don't give up but are persistent in aggressively seeking ways to sell and pursue their innovation.

> *A journey of a thousand miles begins with a single step.*

This proverb is attributed to Confucius. It means that a long journey can seem overwhelming until you start it. Take enough single steps and perhaps you'll arrive.

Some innovations take a long time to bring to fruition because of resistance to change. Machiavelli in 1513 wrote:

> There is nothing more difficult than to take the lead in the introduction of a new order of things. The innovator has for enemies all who have done well under the old conditions, and lukewarm defenders in those who may do well under the new.

7. Hard Working

In my experience over the years at DuPont and elsewhere, I have noted one characteristic that is common to all innovators: an intense interest in working hard at what they were doing. This characteristic is prevalent in needs-driven innovators who work long, hard hours to move their innovations toward reality.

The seven innovator characteristics described in this section are not necessarily innate. To be a successful innovator, it helps for a person to question the status quo; seek alternative solutions to problems; think positively; be action-oriented; recognize that, if nothing is ventured, nothing is gained; be persistent in championing and aggressively pursuing their objectives; and—most importantly—work hard at it.

Kevlar® Innovation Story [14, 15]

The Kevlar innovation story embodies essentially all of the innovative thinking characteristics described above.

Kevlar is a man-made "miracle" fiber five times stronger than steel at equal weight. Applications include bullet-resistant vests and helmets; ropes and cables; sails; fireblocking fabrics; and reinforcement of tires, brake linings, and high-performance composites in aircraft.

Innovative thinking played a vital role in the discovery, development, and commercialization of Kevlar. Importantly, many innovations were critical to the commercial development of the product, and many innovators played essential roles. Together and individually, these innovators exemplified the characteristics and roles of innovators described above.

The Need

In the early 1960s, the DuPont Pioneering Research Laboratory leadership, discontent with the status quo, envisioned a need for a super fiber with the heat resistance of asbestos and the stiffness of glass. The route to achieving these properties was perceived to be through stiff chain polymers.

The Discovery

A breakthrough occurred in 1965 when an innovative research scientist, Stephanie Kwolek, found that the aromatic polyamide, para-aminobenzoic acid, could be polymerized and solubilized under special conditions to yield a rigid-rod polymer. The polymer solution was opaque and watery in appearance. Conventional wisdom implied that the viscosity of the watery solution was much too low to be spinnable into fibers, and the opaque solution would plug spinneret holes. The experienced technician responsible for spinning experimental fibers steadfastly refused to waste time trying to spin this watery, opaque solution.

The environment in the Pioneering Research Laboratory was one that openly encouraged innovators to think positively, take risks, and buck conventional wisdom. Kwolek took a strong positive thinking position, insisting that something unexpected might happen. She vigorously insisted that an attempt be made to spin the solution into a fiber.

Surprisingly, the solution spun well. We now know that the opacity resulted from the formation of polymer liquid crystals that shear-oriented in the spinneret capillaries, yielding well-formed fibers with amazing properties. This discovery was the basis of what later became Kevlar and also catalyzed an entirely new field of scientific research. In 1996, President Clinton awarded Kwolek the National Medal of Technology.

Development

The Kevlar development had many hurdles to overcome. The raw materials used by Kwolek to demonstrate the concept were too costly to justify scale-up. Innovators developed suitable raw materials, but the spinning solvent for the new polymer had to be pure sulfuric acid. Sulfuric acid solutions presented a problem because they were too viscous to spin into fibers at economic speeds. To have a practical process, it was necessary to lower the spinning solution viscosity. The normal approach would be to increase solution temperature but, if this was done, it was expected that sulfuric acid would seriously degrade the polymer.

A major breakthrough came when research scientist Herb Blades went against conventional wisdom. He took a risk and heated the solution to elevated temperatures. Surprisingly, the polymer did not degrade, but unexpectedly formed a previously unknown crystalline complex with sulfuric acid. This invention, coupled with new spinning technology, improved the spinning economics necessary for successful Kevlar commercialization.

The Manufacturing and Engineering Department people charged with designing, building, and running a Kevlar plant took the position that it was impractical to build and operate a plant containing pure sulfuric acid. They insisted that it would be unsafe and corrode equipment.

The technical innovators working on the Kevlar development were persistent about moving ahead. They explained the unusual properties of Kevlar that could lead to many fruitful bottom-line business opportunities. This convinced the engineering and plant people to think more positively about how to deal with the difficulties posed by pure sulfuric acid. The project proceeded, leading to a successful commercial manufacturing plant. *When there is a will, there is a way.*

Commercialization

The Kevlar plant was built in 1982 at a cost of $400 million based on a marketing forecast that Kevlar would replace steel in radial tires. This did not materialize. A Fortune magazine article called Kevlar a miracle without a market.

That Kevlar did not replace steel in radial tires was a serious setback for the business. There was much concern about how to deal with this disappointment. Instead of taking a step backward and mothballing the plant, innovative management stepped forward with a strong positive view about the unique properties of Kevlar and its potential for entirely new product applications.

An intensive, unprecedented research and development (R&D) program was initiated to search for new Kevlar end uses.

New Kevlar End Uses

In the search for new end uses, unexpected problems occurred. For example, one of the anticipated opportunities for Kevlar was to replace steel in ropes and cables. In air, the specific strength of Kevlar is seven times that of steel. In sea water, the specific strength is more than 20 times that of steel. Therefore, it was expected that one could use smaller, lighter, more easily handled lines.

Initial trials using standard rope constructions surprisingly led to Kevlar ropes that were much weaker than steel. Innovator teams tried many alternative constructions and surface lubricants. The end result was Kevlar ropes having more than three times the life of steel in laboratory tests and more than five times in service. This experience led to the realization that the unusual properties of Kevlar would require identifying alternative designs for each end use application.

The challenge to develop new end uses led to many intriguing innovator-driven stories where positive thinking and persistence was an important ingredient for success.

The high modulus and thermal stability of Kevlar led to its consideration in reinforcement applications as an asbestos replacement. This was quickly ruled out by most "experts" because asbestos was cheap and Kevlar was relatively very expensive.

Two staunch innovators took a positive view that there must be a way for Kevlar to replace asbestos in spite of its higher cost. They tried many alternative approaches. The one that succeeded was development of a new form of Kevlar called "pulp." This is made by cutting Kevlar continuous filament fiber into short fibers having a very high surface area. Amazingly, only 1 percent of this new fiber form, uniformly dispersed in a base matrix, provided reinforcement equivalent to over 50 percent of asbestos. This discovery opened the door to major markets for Kevlar as an asbestos replacement in truck and automobile brake linings, gaskets, and hoses.

The outcome of the aggressive program to pursue new Kevlar end uses led to a variety of new products, including bullet-resistant vests and armor that have saved the lives of thousands of law enforcement and military personnel. Today, Kevlar has hundreds of applications, including ropes and cables; sails; fireblocking fabrics; high-performance composites in aircraft; and reinforcement of tires, brake linings, and hoses.

The original failure of Kevlar to replace steel in radial tires was a blessing in disguise because this setback triggered an intensive research and development program leading to many innovations.

Health Care Innovations

The three needs-driven innovations described below highlight many of the important characteristics of innovative thinkers described earlier in this chapter. They also illustrate the vital role of the innovator in recognizing a need, taking concrete steps to meet the need, and championing the innovation through to the adoption stage.

Hospital at Home Care[16]

Summary of the Program

The Hospital at Home program provides hospital-level care, including daily physician and nurse visits, diagnostic testing, and treatment in a patient's home as a full substitute for acute hospital care for selected conditions that are common among seniors. Studies have shown that the Hospital at Home program results in shorter lengths of stay, lower costs and readmission rates, and fewer complications than does traditional inpatient care. Surveys indicate higher levels of patient and family member satisfaction than with traditional care.

The Need

Dr. Bruce Leff, Professor of Medicine at the Johns Hopkins University School of Medicine, observed that hospitalization for older patients resulted in complications such as infections acquired in the hospital and medical errors, as well as functional decline and delirium. He recognized the need to change the status quo and took steps to initiate a home-based hospital-level care program with the potential to reduce these adverse outcomes.

The Needs-Driven Innovation

Leff implemented the concept of Hospital at Home Care in 2001. The innovation was first piloted with 17 patients at the Johns Hopkins Bayview Medical Center, where it demonstrated that the program was feasible, safe, and cost-effective.

The Hospital at Home Care innovation provides complete substitution of an acute hospital stay in the patient's home. Patient eligibility for in-home hospital care is assessed in the health care setting. Eligible patients are transported home by ambulance and receive initial and daily visits by a physician, continuous nursing support, home health equipment and services, diagnostic testing, and other services. To evaluate the program in a broader range of settings, a study was conducted in three cities: two in Medicare managed-care organizations in Worcester, MA and Buffalo, NY, and one in a Veteran's Administration health center in Portland, OR.

A project team is working to disseminate the model to would-be adopters and developing protocols for Hospital at Home treatment for additional conditions, including urinary tract infection, urosepsis, volume depletion/dehydration, and deep vein thrombosis/pulmonary embolism.

Results

Studies have shown that the Hospital at Home innovation results in shorter lengths of stay, lower costs and readmission rates, and fewer complications than does traditional inpatient care. Surveys indicate higher levels of patient and family member satisfaction than with traditional care.

Use by Other Organizations

The New Orleans Veterans Administration started a hospital at home model in late 2007. Presbyterian Health Systems, a large managed care organization in New Mexico, started the program in 2008, while United Healthcare is planning to pilot the model in its Arizona market. Other Veterans Administration and Medicare-managed care organizations are contemplating adoption.

After planning began in April 2007, Presbyterian Health Services, led by Lesley Cryer, RN, Executive Director of Presbyterian's Home HealthCare Services, succeeded in admitting its first patient to Hospital at Home in October 2008.

Other health systems around the country have shown interest and expect several additional major adoptions. In addition, there has been strong international interest in the model.

Household Program in Nursing Homes[17]

Summary of the Program

This innovation provides elders with an alternative to nursing homes and traditional assisted living facilities. These communities provide groups of elders with a comfortable, warm home environment and staff who provide the highest level of clinical care while nurturing relationships and elders' autonomy. Evaluations suggest that elders receive equal or higher quality of care and report better quality of life than residents of nursing homes. Since redesigning the Meadowlark Hills nursing home to reflect the home-environment approach, more people have wanted to live there. By 2008, the facility was completely full with a 300-person waiting list. In spite of its many advantages, however, nursing home leaders are often reluctant to make major changes, fearing that "it can't be done" or that government regulators will object.

The Need

As new President and CEO of Meadowlark Hills retirement community in Manhattan, KS, Steve Shields was dissatisfied with the institutional feel and effect on residents' health of the traditional nursing home model in which elderly residents become socially inactive and vacant eyed. He recognized the need to create an environment in which residents direct their own lives, enabling them to continue to grow as individuals.

The Needs-Driven Innovation

Shields created and implemented the innovative concept of
a Household Program in Nursing Homes that improves residents' health status, reduces staff turnover, and boosts demand
for services.

To implement his concept, Shields formed a steering committee
of 12 formal and informal leaders of the Meadowlark community.
The committee conducted many studies and developed a strategic plan. As a result, Meadowlark Hills in 2001 renovated one of
its facilities so that residents can live together in group households and become more independent.

An architectural redesign replaced the standard nursing home
layout (long hallways, nursing stations, and one dining hall) with
six "households" having 12 to 25 beds each. Each household has
its own living room, dining room, kitchen, porch, and patio, as
well as staff that attend to residents' medical, dietary, and housekeeping needs. Residents choose when they wake up and go to
sleep, when and what they eat, and the activities in which they
want to participate.

Results

The change in approach to nursing homes led to improvements
in residents' health, a sharp decrease in staff turnover, and a
significant increase in demand for facility services, all without
raising operating costs.

Since the redesign at Meadowlark Hills, more people in the community have wanted to live there. In 1997, about 12 percent of
beds were vacant; by 2008, the facility was completely full and
had a 300-person waiting list. Nursing home officials from 42
states and 14 countries have visited Meadowlark Hills seeking
ideas they can apply at their own facilities.

Use by Other Organizations

Innovator Steve Shields continues to champion the concept of the Household Program in Nursing Homes innovation. Despite the program's many advantages, however, nursing home leaders are often reluctant to make major changes, fearing that it can't be done or that government regulators will object. For example, resistance to change is high in the State of Florida, which has a very large population of elderly people and numerous nursing homes.

Real-Time Surgery Tracking[18]

Summary of the Program

The Regional Medical Center in Vineland, NJ revised its process for tracking the status of operating rooms to efficiently update staff and surgeons about surgical procedures that are in progress, thus allowing them to fill available gaps in the schedule and quickly respond to delays in room turnover. The new process provides real-time information to all interested parties electronically via a computerized status board that uses color codes to distinguish the different phases of the perioperative patient's journey, with flashing alerts that indicate delays. As a result of this real-time operating room tracking system, Regional Medical Center increased the use of its operating rooms (from 70 to 82%), reduced the number of cases started late in the day, and achieved faster room turnover and pharmaceutical restocking in operating rooms.

The Need

The Regional Medical Center had an existing computerized surgery scheduling system but used a manual chalkboard system to track actual operating room (OR) usage. This cumbersome, time-consuming system led to a number of problems, including unused capacity, delays in room turnover, and high levels of staff and surgeon dissatisfaction. The OR medical director and the director of surgical services recognized an important need to innovatively increase efficiency of the OR.

The Needs-Driven Innovation

The approach was for Regional Medical Center to change its process of OR tracking from a manual system in which staff members walked around to gather information about procedure timing to a computerized status board in which OR procedures are tracked using a color-coded scheme to highlight each phase of the intraoperative period; alerts are generated when delays occur, allowing proactive response. The status board is displayed on large flat screens hung in various central locations to ensure that updated information is available to all interested parties on a real-time basis. The status board is updated electronically throughout the day.

Implementing this innovation required no new staff members. Several innovative individuals—notably the medical director, the director of surgical services, and the Surgical Services Executive Committee member who created the program— incorporated their work on the OR tracking system into their daily activities.

Regarding costs, three large flat screen LCD monitors, at a cost of $3,000, were placed in key locations. No other hardware was needed because each surgical suite already had a small monitor on which the electronic status board could be displayed.

Results

As a result of the real-time OR tracking system, Regional Medical Center substantially increased utilization of its ORs, reduced the number of cases started late in the day, and achieved faster room turnover and pharmaceutical restocking of ORs.

Chapter 4

Innovative Problem Solving

When health care innovators identify a need that they are energized to pursue, it's of value to convene a team of diverse thinkers and apply the innovative problem solving process. A team approach to problem solving can also be the first step toward implementation since a team effort is usually required to put the innovative solution into action.

Three-Step Process

There are many problem solving processes described in the literature. I favor a process that has three steps:

1. Define the Problem / *Core focus areas*

2. Generate and Harvest Ideas / *Creativity skills*

3. Plan Actions / *Roadmap*

The first step involves defining the problem, which may require identifying some core focus areas. The second step involves generating and evaluating ideas. The third step involves planning actions to take the best idea to reality. In dealing with important needs-driven issues, it's often of value to have a design meeting before beginning the innovative problem solving process.

Design Meeting

The design meeting is attended by the innovator who initiated the project, a facilitator, and a few other critically important people. A key outcome is to agree on participants, the problem statement, and potential focus areas. Another purpose of the meeting is to agree on logistics such as length of the process, number of participants, location, and dates. The design meeting should be held several weeks in advance of the kickoff to enable scheduling of invited participants.

Facilitator

A competent facilitator can make the difference between success and failure. The role of the facilitator is to lead the problem solving process, control group dynamics, and guide process flow. Good facilitators keep the process on track, improvise process changes as required, sense the best creativity tools to apply, let everyone have equal time, and assist in harvesting team output.

Participants

Selection of participants is a critical factor in a successful outcome of the team problem solving session. The number of participants might vary from 4 to 12, depending on the nature of the issue being addressed.

Participants should include the innovator; a decisionmaker who would be in a position to assign resources, if warranted; a facilitator; people knowledgeable about the issue; potential implementers of harvested ideas; and at least one "wild card." A wild card is a person known to be an energetic creative thinker, but who is not familiar with the issue being addressed.

If the issue relates to health care, the team might include nurses, doctors, interns, patients, or administration officials. Sometimes it would be of value to invite special guests from other health care locations.

While creative thinking skills are important in successful problem solving, another essential ingredient is diversity. Hence, in selecting participants, attention should be paid to people with diverse thinking preferences, e.g., right versus left brain, and different creativity styles, e.g., adaptive versus innovative. Diversity in thinking is discussed in Chapter 6.

After the design meeting, it is time to begin the three-step problem solving process.

Define the Problem

A vital step in the problem solving process is to identify, within the broad problem statement, the core problem where idea generation is most likely to pay off. This step is sometimes the most challenging, but it is essential to focus on the area most amenable to creative thinking.

Sometimes the problem statement is specific enough that it encompasses a core issue, enabling the team to delve directly into generating and harvesting ideas. These sessions usually take a couple of hours. Alternatively, sometimes the problem statement is so broad that it's difficult to productively apply creative thinking tools. For example, the problem statement might be…

"How can we reduce health care costs?"

In this case, the session leader might ask…

"What stands in the way of reducing health care costs?"

This would likely lead to many possible core focus areas that the group can boil down to three or four. The next step is to decide on one focus area to attack, or to organize into separate teams, each choosing a different focus area.

There are several other ways to develop focus areas. A technique popular with many facilitators is to ask participants to think about a beneficial outcome related to the broad problem statement by completing the sentence:

Wouldn't it be nice if (WIBNI)?

For example, if the broad problem statement was:

How can we enhance our recruitment program?

a WIBNI might be:

Wouldn't it be nice if all potential recruits have personalized treatment during their visit?

The focus area would then be stated as:

How can we personalize the program for all recruits prior to and during their visit?

Generate and Harvest Ideas

Once a core focus issue is selected, then creative juices can begin to flow, as the team generates many ideas related to the stated focus area. It's best to start with team members expressing ideas within normal thinking patterns. This has the benefit of collecting good ideas that people may have brought to the meeting. It's a good warmup.

When the flow of ideas is exhausted using normal thinking patterns, and no idea is generated that "rings the bell," the facilitator reviews creative thinking techniques. Facilitators have different preferences regarding the tools they find most effective and feel comfortable facilitating. The objective is to stir up a new round of idea generation. Several productive creative thinking tools are described in the next chapter.

Each team member can write his or her ideas on 3"x 5" Post-it notes, read the ideas out loud to help trigger other people's ideas, and hand the notes to the facilitator for posting on a hang chart. Individual thinking, followed by idea sharing, motivates everyone to participate.

A problem solving session will often generate 50-150 ideas posted on hang charts. This includes ideas generated by both pattern thinking and creativity techniques. The challenge is to harvest the ideas the team views as most worthy to implement.

The selection process varies. The team might formulate criteria such as health care impact, feasibility, and uniqueness. Team members might individually examine the ideas and vote for the ones they consider the most valuable. The list often boils down to three to six ideas for further discussion. Finally, two to three ideas are usually selected for careful evaluation and upgrading before deciding on implementation. The Six Thinking Hats framework, described in Chapter 5, Innovative Thinking Techniques, is a powerful way to evaluate and upgrade ideas in a productive, effective way.

Plan Actions

Problem solving sessions will be most productive if sufficient time is devoted to an implementation plan for best ideas. Otherwise, sessions are concluded with good ideas, but the ideas are lost when people return to urgent matters at their desks. This is why it's vital to have the innovator organize and participate in the session, along with an administrator who has authority to assign resources, if deemed appropriate.

In taking ideas to reality, several innovator characteristics described in Chapter 3 come into play. Sometimes the innovator takes steps to move an idea to reality as a one-person team. At other times, teams are involved where the innovator takes a leading position.

There are three core elements that work together in taking ideas to reality:

- The Innovation Team
- Leadership Sponsorship
- The Innovation Roadmap

The innovator and participating team provide the horsepower for doing the work. The administration leadership ensures support, strategic guidance, and an ongoing supply of resources. The roadmap lays out the path for the innovative team to follow. When properly structured, these three elements will reinforce each other and accelerate the rate of progress. The leadership effectively staffs the team. The team continually upgrades the roadmap. The roadmapping process prepares the leadership to supply resources to the team at critical moments.

Jazz Musicians as a Model for Innovative Teams

A fascinating perspective about spontaneous innovation and innovative teams is provided by a novel jazz-band tape, featuring Bobby Bradford and friends, that was recorded by Stan Gryskiewicz of the Center for Creative Leadership.[19]

Some of the points made in this tape are applicable to dynamic industrial and health care teams:

- Successful innovators invent the concept and bring it to reality.
- Risk-taking abounds.

Key points in the tape:

- Innovation does not occur in a vacuum.
  Street musicians blended African and European musical forms. The result was "the blues."

- Goal and role clarity are key.
  The leader assembles a group with musical competencies.
  The leader does not write down the notes or tell each member when to play each note.
  Goal clarity of the group is essential, but each player exercises individuality and improvisation.
  The leader is continuously balancing tension between team and individual behavior.

- Risk-taking abounds.
  Team members are encouraged to improvise innovatively.
  "Control" is partially lost and mistakes made.
  The group expects mistakes and prepares itself to "dance on a slippery floor."

- Successful innovations lead to successful imitations.

   Successful imitators innovatively reconcile the new musical ideas with music "to which the public could dance."

   There are many variations on the new theme.

- An individual can make profound changes in the world.

   Charlie Parker, Louis Armstrong, Duke Ellington

- Successful innovators invent the concept and bring it to reality.

   First reaction to something new is to squelch it.

   Be-bop in original form sounded like playing with "a mouthful of hot rice." It opened the door to further advances.

A book by Charles Prather, Ph.D., *The Manager's Guide to Fostering Innovation and Creativity in Teams*,[20] is excellent relative to the above subject, and I highly recommend it.

Health Care Innovations

All successful innovations are the result of a problem solving process where a lead innovator and team address a need, generate ideas to meet the need, and implement a strategy that accomplishes the innovation.

Knowledge of the various elements of the creative problem solving process, like those described in this chapter, and the creative thinking techniques described in the next chapter, will be helpful as teams pursue the innovation process. Three successful health care innovations that followed key elements in the problem solving process are discussed below.

Medical Team Training in the Military [21]

Summary of the Program

A comprehensive medical team training program supported by crew resource management principles adopted from the aviation industry was developed and implemented in 79 Veterans Affairs Medical Centers (VAMCs). A review of 10 participating facilities showed measurable improvement in communication and patient care. The national rollout of the comprehensive medical team training program to all acute care VAMCs began in January 2007.

The Need

Many communication failures in VAMCs lead to adverse events. A review of more than 14,000 root-cause analysis reports submitted to the Veterans Affairs (VA) National Center for Patient Safety found that communication failures were involved in more than 75 percent of adverse events. Communication failure has been identified as a pivotal factor in nearly two-thirds of sentinel events reported by a Joint Commission since 1995. Hence, there was a clear need to substantially reduce communication failures.

The Needs-Driven Innovation

Jim Bagian, a physician, former astronaut, and founder of The National Center for Patient Safety, recognized the seriousness of the communication failures. To solve this problem, he took steps to establish an innovative organizational structure for patient safety operations in VAMCs.

With Bagian's encouragement and support, Dr. Ed Dunn, a cardiothoracic surgeon, led the development and subsequent implementation of the Medical Team Training program beginning in 2003 with pilot facilities, leading up to a national rollout beginning in January 2007. The Medical Team Training program translates communication principles and behaviors embedded in aviation culture to health care organizations in the Veterans Health System. The premise of the program is to use clinical examples in health care environments to deliver a peer-to-peer message of change from physicians and nurse faculty members.

Human resources are the most valuable asset in this program. National Center for Patient Safety staff include physicians, nurses, and professionals. These individuals manage program operations, provide consultation and followup to program participants, and collect data and engage in analysis to evaluate program results. Facility-based staff include an interdisciplinary team of 8 to 12 health care professionals who incur the opportunity cost of giving their time and effort to the implementation of the Medical Team Training program. For surgical groups, there is an additional opportunity cost of closing the OR and surgical clinics on the day of the learning sessions.

Medical Team Training learning sessions include three faculty members per session. These faculty members also spend one day preparing for the session and traveling to the training site. The National Center for Patient Safety provides faculty members with two to three months of training.

Results

Although surgical staff — surgeons, anesthesiologists, and surgical nurses — expressed concern that Medical Team Training activities such as briefings and debriefings would add time to procedures and complicate their already busy days, collective experiences to date suggest that such concerns are ill-founded. In some facilities, productivity and throughput have actually increased, which some have attributed to reduced waiting time for instruments, equipment, radiographs, and surgical assistants, along with the timely resolution of other issues that have been identified in preoperative briefings guided by specialty-specific checklists.

Use by Other Organizations

The National Center for Patient Safety Medical Team Training program is in the midst of a national rollout in the Veterans Health System. The target audience is all VAMCs providing acute care services. The National Center for Patient Safety has facilitated 99 learning sessions in 79 facilities for 7,070 participants with an average of 75 attendees per session in VAMCs across the country.

Therapy for Brain-Injured Patients [22]

Summary of the Program

The Mayo Clinic provides remote cognitive rehabilitation sessions to patients who have had an acquired brain injury. Using an Internet-based, secure instant messaging platform, an office-based therapist conducts the rehabilitation session with the patient, who remains in or near his or her home. Both patients and therapists report high levels of satisfaction with the program, which has enhanced access to rehabilitation services for patients who otherwise would find it difficult to travel to clinic facilities.

The Need

Patients who suffer an acquired brain injury often require cognitive therapy to regain memory and other cognitive deficits lost from the injury, but many patients find it difficult to travel to such sessions and thus miss out on this valuable service. There was a need to help patients with traumatic brain injuries through better coordination of health services.

The Needs-Driven Innovation

To deal with this needs-driven problem, the Mayo Clinic provides remote cognitive rehabilitation sessions to patients who have had an acquired brain injury using an Internet-based, secure instant messaging platform. An office-based therapist conducts the rehabilitation session with the patient, who remains in or near his or her home.

Results

Both patients and therapists report high levels of satisfaction with the program, which has enhanced access to rehabilitation services for parents who otherwise would find it difficult to travel to clinic facilities

Use by Other Organizations

Although many other centers are conducting telerehabilitation, to our knowledge, this is the only study of its type being conducted with this population in this manner.

Osteoporosis Healthy Bones Program[23]

Summary of the Program

Kaiser Permanente Southern California developed the Healthy Bones Model of Care program to proactively identify, screen, and treat those with or at risk for osteoporosis, and hence reduce the risk of costly, debilitating fractures. With the support of information technology (IT) systems that identify enrollees with gaps in care, care managers and clinicians proactively reach out to those in need of screening to schedule a bone density scan. Scan results are interpreted immediately and those requiring additional services receive, as appropriate, education on osteoporosis, a prescription for medication to improve bone density, and referrals for additional support.

The Need

Ten million Americans have osteoporosis, with another 34 million being at risk of developing the disease. Because bone density tends to decline with age, the prevalence of osteoporosis is likely to increase significantly as the population ages. Osteoporosis frequently leads to debilitating, expensive fractures from which individuals often never fully recover. An innovation was needed to screen and treat at-risk individuals to reduce the risk of fractures.

The Needs-Driven Innovation

A Healthy Bones Model of Care program was designed to proactively identify, screen, and treat those with or at risk for osteoporosis. With the support of IT systems that identify patients with gaps in osteoporosis care, Kaiser care managers and clinicians proactively reach out to those in need of screening to schedule them for a bone density scan. Scan results are interpreted immediately. Those requiring services receive osteoporosis education, a prescription for medication to improve bone density, and/or referrals to additional needed support during the same visit.

Results

The program significantly increased screening and treatment rates, leading to a 41 percent reduction in hip fractures, more than 250 saved lives each year, and an estimated $39.5 million reduction in the annual treatment costs for such fractures, a figure that far outweighs program costs.

Use by Other Organizations

Some form of this program has been implemented in every Kaiser region in the nation. In addition, Geisinger Clinic, Cleveland Clinic, and the Mayo Clinic have adopted similar programs. Outside the United States, organizations in the United Kingdom, Australia, and Canada have adopted the Fracture Liaison Program which uses many of the same program elements.

Chapter 5
Innovative Thinking Techniques

Innovative thinking aids all human endeavors.

Health care innovators seeking to generate ideas to meet a need will benefit by becoming acquainted with the many creative thinking techniques that are available. Some of the most productive ones are described in this chapter.

Donald W. MacKinnon, University of California, wrote:

> During most of man's literate history, creative behavior has been thought to be artistic behavior and rather especially the writing of poetry, although the work of painter and sculptor were recognized early as being in the same class. The view that writing of poetry is a matter of artistry has been expanded to include the idea that scientists as well as many others in their endeavors can also be creative persons employing, as does the artist, the creative process.

This quote makes the salient point that not only poets, painters, and sculptors can be innovative, but that all persons can think innovatively as they pursue their human endeavors. Innovative thinking is an essential ingredient in all innovations and human endeavors, both in generating the original idea and in overcoming barriers to bring the idea to reality. Innovative thinking does not replace information, training, logic, or hard work but is another factor in getting the job done better. It's an important element in the continuous improvement framework where steady incremental improvements, as well as breakthrough advances, are important.

It is a myth that creativity is limited to a few individuals who are naturally creative. In reality, creativity is a skill. It's a skill that can be learned and applied like any other skill. Research with fraternal and identical twins supports the view that different abilities to think creatively are not inherited.[24] Thinking and creative thinking are learnable skills like driving a car, swimming, golfing, or knitting. Some people will be better at certain things than others but, given sufficient motivation, instruction, and practice, everyone can raise his or her level of skill.

In solving difficult problems and searching for new opportunities, our natural tendency is to build from our longstanding experience base. It often works, but sometimes it doesn't. This type of approach—linear thinking—is important and a logical starting point, particularly in traditional cost cutting and quality improvement programs. But there is another approach. When our traditional linear thinking methods do not bring the results we want, we need to look at things in a new way.

Breaking away from traditional thinking is more easily said than done. This is illustrated humorously in the movie *Dead Poets Society*. In this movie, Robin Williams, playing an instructor at a prep school, tells students to tear out introductory pages in their poetry book. Tearing pages from a book goes against the norm. It's humorous to watch the students' shocked faces as they struggle against stepping outside the paradigm that tearing pages from a book is "sinful."

In another scene, Robin Williams demonstrates his approach to looking at the world differently. He tells his students to jump on top of their desks and look around from that vantage point. He comments:

> Break out…look around you…dare to strike out and
> find new ground.

We don't have to jump on top of desks or tables to look at the world differently. There exist deliberate, systematic tools for innovative thinking that help us break away from normal thinking patterns. These tools can be learned and applied as can any skill.

Pattern-Breaking Tools

Six productive creative thinking tools with examples of practical application are described below.

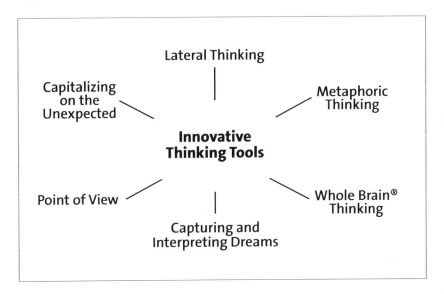

Lateral Thinking

In my experience, lateral thinking is the most productive tool to help break away from traditional thinking. It is described in several books by Dr. Edward de Bono[25-27] and taught in certification courses for training of trainers.[28] Lateral thinking is defined in the Oxford English Dictionary as follows:

> Seeking ways to solve problems by apparently illogical means.

de Bono's book, *Mechanism of Mind*,[5] first published in 1969, is a classic in the field of creative thinking. It explains that the mind is a self-organizing information system. As our mind absorbs information and digests experiences, our thinking organizes itself into patterns based on these inputs.

Pattern thinking is essential. Otherwise, we would have to rethink each morning whether we put our shoes on before our socks or our socks on before our shoes. We would have to re-learn how to walk. In tackling problems or searching for new opportunities, it is sensible to start out with normal patterns of thinking. This generally provides many useful ideas. But to solve difficult problems or conceive radically new concepts that require a new direction in thinking, it is often necessary to step outside our normal patterns of thinking. Some refer to this as "thinking outside the box."

Visualize, in the figure below, tackling a difficult problem and racing "linearly" down a highway going east, the direction of thinking that you perceive might lead to a solution.

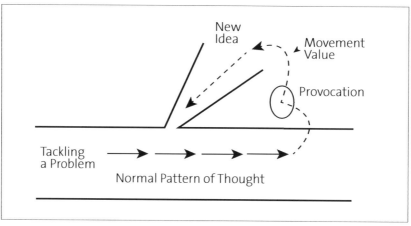

Reprinted with permission. ©2012. I P Development Corporation.
Published by de Bono Thinking Systems®.

If there is a side road going north, you would likely speed past it, even though it might lead to a wider, faster highway and take you to your destination sooner.

There are ways to test these side roads in problem solving or opportunity searching that might lead to better, more novel ideas. A productive approach is to create "provocations" that jar us outside our normal patterns of thinking. Provocations are thoughts that are related to the issue being attacked, but that are illogical or unstable. They are bizarre, impractical, ridiculous, or challenging.

Instead of rejecting a provocation, we can learn to use it for its forward effect as a stepping stone to shift laterally out of standard linear patterns of thinking. This process creates a new starting point to address the problem and always leads to a flow of new, useful ideas.

Dr. de Bono teaches several techniques that systematically help generate provocations:

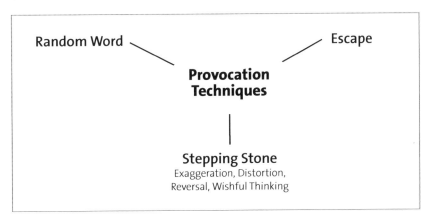

Random Word involves creating a new "entry point" by selecting a word at random, e.g., a noun from a dictionary or poster that is not connected to the subject.

Escape involves examining the subject for what we take for granted and then canceling, negating, or escaping from some of the things we take for granted.

Stepping Stone involves the exaggeration, distortion, reversal, or wishful thinking about a subject that is a stepping stone to new ideas.

Application

The lateral thinking process involves three steps:

1. Selection of a focus area requiring creative new ideas.

2. Development of provocations relating to the focus area using lateral thinking techniques.

3. Generation of sensible ideas dealing with the problem, stimulated by the provocation.

The bolder the provocation, the better the chance that it will lead to many unusual ideas. The challenge is to generate several provocations and ideas until one excites enthusiasm. A productive lateral thinking session is one that generates at least one "great" idea worth implementing!

Learning the lateral thinking techniques is a first step. Applying these techniques in a practical way after leaving the classroom or lecture is another matter. Several examples are described to illustrate the lateral thinking process.

Innovative Cost Reduction

This example illustrates how a need to reduce costs led a team to apply lateral thinking to the issue and save over $500,000 annually.

A corporate information systems team was dealing with this need:

> How can we reduce costs in the information systems function?

The group manager had attended a lateral thinking workshop and decided to hold a meeting to apply her learning to this problem. When the flow of ideas was exhausted using pattern thinking, she explained lateral thinking to the group. Many new ideas were generated.

The lateral thinking technique that paid off in this case was reversal. It led to this provocation:

> Reduce costs by spending more money.

This provocation generated the idea that spending more money on fewer equipment vendors would provide leverage to obtain large discounts. The approach was to cut the number of vendors and negotiate better prices on high-volume orders. This idea led to an annual savings of more than $300,000. The concept was applied to maintenance and saved a similar amount. Hence, a 2-hour lateral thinking session provided an annual savings of over $500,000. Over a 10-year period, savings would amount to over $5 million.

Plant Computerization Risk

A plant technical group, working jointly with manufacturing and the engineering department, had developed a prototype for computerizing the complex Nomex plant process. They were at the stage of purchasing and installing plant-scale equipment. An innovative technical manager skilled in lateral thinking convinced colleagues to have a creative problem solving session to address this needs-driven challenge:

> How can we install the computer system in the plant much faster and at a substantially lower cost than forecasted?

The problem solving session precipitated many provocations. The one that paid off used the "escape" technique:

> *Eliminate* the Engineering Department.

This provocation led to the risky idea to skip the normal step of preassembling hardware and software at the Engineering Department Laboratory and ship the entire computer system directly to the plant where it would be integrated directly into the plant process. The team took the view—*nothing ventured, nothing gained*—and took the risk to implement this idea.

This approach succeeded, accelerating installation of the new computer system by about 2 years and saving more than $1 million in development costs. This innovative approach became a model for risk taking and value partnering between functions.

Application in Education

A team of educators in southern Delaware invited me to do a seminar for a graduating class of about 100 high school students with the objective of introducing them to creative thinking skills. To illustrate the process and capture their attention, I selected this needs-driven issue:

> How can we make learning in the classroom more fun?

I first explained lateral thinking, then asked the audience to apply this technique to the problem. All students participated by interaction with their neighbor. A group of six volunteers sat at a table up front that was equipped with loudspeakers. Many provocations were developed using lateral thinking.

Wishful thinking led to this provocation:

> Eliminate teachers.

This provocation triggered the idea that once a month the teacher would become part of the student group and a student or team of students would take turns conducting the lesson. Several teachers in the audience said they would seriously consider implementing this idea.

Speed of Delivery of an Innovation

This example illustrates how lateral thinking was applied to generate an idea for commercializing a new nylon product in record time.

A research and development unit had made a technical breakthrough that would enable economic manufacture of a proprietary new product innovation. This was a high-priority program. The organization was anxious to move this product to market much faster than the normal development cycle. A cross-functional team applied lateral thinking to address this needs-driven issue:

> How can we move the new product to market faster?

The provocation technique that paid off was random word. The random word was "beach," selected from a billboard bathing suit advertisement. Thinking about "beach" led to a series of thoughts relating to water, to swimming, to swim meets, and to competition. The thought of competition triggered this provocation:

> Give the breakthrough technology to our
> toughest competitor.

This was certainly provocative! It triggered thinking about who was the toughest competitor and how it would bring this breakthrough to market. The toughest competitor in this case was a Japanese company known to move new products to market rapidly.

Questioning how the competitor would handle this breakthrough led to an idea about an organizational structure quite different from the prevailing culture. The idea was accepted by marketing, engineering, manufacturing, and business functions after much discussion, despite some difficult turf issues. The product was introduced 2 to 3 years faster than normal. This saved millions of dollars in development costs and enabled early assessment of the product in the marketplace.

Growing a Business

This example illustrates how lateral and metaphoric thinking generated unusual ideas to aid in meeting a need to grow a business faster.

A business unit had started up a new plant in Europe and therefore had much higher capacity than it had sales. There was an urgent need to take steps to increase sales. The innovative business director was familiar with the problem solving process and requested his strategic planning team to organize a session to address the needs-driven issue:

> How can we grow our business faster?

A multifunctional team consisting of marketing, technical, manufacturing, strategic business planners, and two wild cards was convened. As noted earlier, a wild card is a person known to be a creative thinker, but who is unfamiliar with the issue being addressed, and hence brings a fresh point of view.

Most of the participants had attended creative thinking seminars and workshops and were eager to apply their learning to a high-stakes, practical issue. Facilitators trained in problem solving and creative thinking techniques were enlisted to lead the session. Many innovative focus areas were identified:

- What new products can we develop?
- How can we improve existing products?
- What new applications might we develop?
- What new markets can we penetrate?
- How might we increase our customer base?

The group was divided into subgroups to generate ideas in each of the focus areas. When the flow of ideas using normal thinking patterns was exhausted, the subgroups applied creative thinking techniques to generate additional ideas. Lateral thinking and metaphoric thinking paid off, yielding many unusual ideas judged to be of value.

Lateral thinking generated this provocation:

Don't sell the product.

This led to the concept of leasing the product. This was feasible for many of the products in this business. This idea would likely never have been thought of using normal thinking patterns.

Metaphoric thinking, discussed later in this section, led to this question:

How are trees and shrubs grown?

This thought led to the concept of pruning. The idea was to "prune" customers that were forecast to have low growth rates. This would free up technical service and marketing resources to grow the business faster by better servicing customers forecast to have high growth rates.

Innovative Process

This example illustrates how lateral thinking helped solve a serious process problem with a filter system in the Kevlar plant.

A team of R&D, manufacturing, and engineering staffers was dealing with this needs-driven focus area:

> How can we improve continuity of our complex, continuous-flow filter system?

The filter system relied on a reciprocating belt with 70 moving parts that kept breaking down. The group manager was a creativity champion whose group was educated in lateral thinking. A reversal provocation paid off:

> The moving belt is stationary.

This new mindset shifted thinking in an entirely new direction and led to the design of an innovative new process that reduced the number of moving parts by 80 percent. The result was a major breakthrough in process continuity and product quality and led to significant cost savings.

Metaphoric Thinking

Metaphoric thinking is another powerful creative thinking technique. It involves searching for systems or problems that are unrelated, but in some ways similar, to the problem under attack. The challenge is to understand how the problem was solved in another system, which often leads to new ideas about the system under attack.

Sometimes understanding how nature solved a related problem yields many useful ideas. Dr. Jonas Salk was quoted in Plauh's *The 9 Natural Laws of Leadership* as saying:

> I try to think like nature to find the right questions. You don't invent the answers, you reveal the answers from nature. In nature the answers to our problems already exist. Ask how nature would solve this problem.

Two examples below illustrate where metaphoric thinking was successfully applied.

Nomex® Colorguard

This example describes how an innovation-driven researcher, who had attended creativity seminars, applied metaphoric thinking to solve a difficult technical problem. His creative thinking led to an important product innovation.

Nomex aramid fiber is inherently flame resistant and is used in protective clothing, electrical insulation, and honeycomb aircraft panels. To expand Nomex markets into flame-resistant fabrics for drapes, upholstery, and carpets, a need existed to develop a product that could be dyed in customers' mills without special procedures. Because the fiber had a very tight structure, the dyeing process required swelling agents that were costly and caused environmental problems. Many research programs failed to accomplish the objective of a readily dyeable Nomex.

An innovative research scientist working on the Nomex dyeing problem had attended creativity seminars that described many creative thinking techniques, including metaphoric thinking. He applied this technique to the problem. He asked himself:

> What in nature has a tight structure, but can be penetrated—and how?

His answer:

> The earth!—Coal miners gain access to the interior of the earth by digging holes and propping them open.

Inspired by this metaphor, he added a large organic molecule to the fiber structure during manufacture to prop open the structure of the forming Nomex fiber. This allowed entrance of dyes under standard mill conditions. The dye entered, the props collapsed, and the dyes stayed in the fiber.

A dyeable, flame-resistant Nomex, trademarked Colorguard®, was commercialized, creating many potential new applications for Nomex in colorful, flame-retardant upholstery, drapes, and carpets.

Dust Reduction

This example illustrates how metaphoric thinking stimulated ideas to meet the need for an innovative way to reduce copious amounts of dust in a plant.

A manufacturing team was dealing with serious cost and quality problems across the plant, caused by dust generated in one of their processes. They had developed a long list of ideas to reduce the dust, but none were very good. Several members of the team had attended creative thinking workshops and suggested a creative thinking session to attack this needs-driven problem:

How can we reduce dust in our plant?

The technique that paid off was metaphoric thinking. They questioned:

How does nature remove dust from the environment?

They reasoned that one way that nature removes dust from the environment is by heavy rainfall. This thought shifted their thinking in an entirely new direction that generated creative ideas on ways to remove dust through a watering-systems approach.

Whole Brain® Thinking

Chapter 6, *Diversity in Thinking*, describes the Herrmann Brain Dominance Instrument® (HBDI®), which integrates the scientific study of the brain with the study of creative human development. The basic concept of the Herrmann® model is a metaphor for the brain composed of four interactive quadrants, each representing a different category of thinking preferences. These four quadrants are described in Chapter 6:

- The upper left, (A) blue quadrant may prefer performing analytical, logical, and mathematical activities.
- The upper right, (D) yellow quadrant may prefer imaginative, intuitive, and risky tasks or activities.
- The lower left, (B) green quadrant may prefer structured, sequential and (or) organized mental activities.
- The lower right, (C) red quadrant may prefer interpersonal and (or) spiritual activities.

For most of us, there is a brain dominance condition in which the quadrants work together, but with one or two taking the lead. Combined together, these four quadrants represent Whole Brain® Thinking. The HBDI® Assessment has 120 questions that measures the degree of thinking preferences in each quadrant.

Applications

There are many practical applications for the brain dominance concept, including problem solving, strategic business planning, and interpersonal relationships.

The Problem Solving Walk-Around™

A new perspective about a problem might be gained by viewing it from the different modes of thinking. An individual or team might ask "How would my problem be viewed with sequential focus on each of the quadrants?"

"Walking around" the problem might provide new insights toward a solution. The framework:

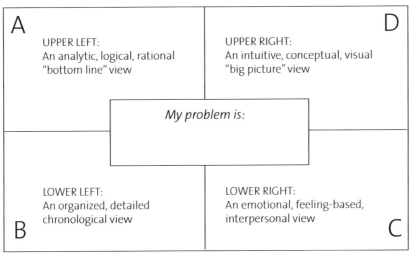

The following example illustrates how the problem solving Walk-Around™ was applied to tackle a corporate issue.

One of the themes in a DuPont Company worldwide leadership meeting with 400 attendees was the importance of diversity in achieving the corporate vision. Ned Herrmann was invited to deliver a keynote address outlining brain dominance theory and provided feedback on the HBDI® Assessment that all participants had taken prior to the meeting.

To illustrate the value of brain dominance theory in problem solving, a 2-hour session for a portion of the audience was held using the problem solving Walk-Around™. This framework was structured with a set of questions in each quadrant designed to stimulate Whole Brain® Thinking on the central issue of—*How to educate DuPonters about the value of creativity and innovation*— as shown below:

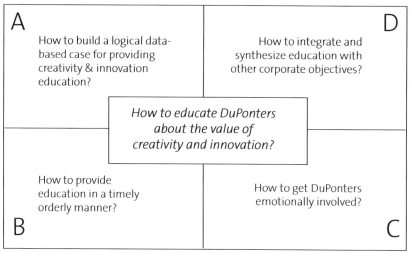

Additional applications are discussed in Chapter 6, *Diversity in Thinking*, including the value of Whole Brain® Thinking in interpersonal relationships, innovative problem solving, and operation of a strategic planning team.

Capturing and Interpreting Dreams

Capturing and interpreting dreams is a Ned Herrmann technique for harnessing the subconscious. It's a way to seed new ideas, solve problems, and envision new opportunities.

Have you ever experienced going to sleep with a problem and waking up the next morning with a clearer view of the problem and new approaches to solving it? This happens because the mind continues to function while we sleep. In the subconscious state, the mind is less inhibited.

The *Applied Creative Thinking* workshop sponsored by Herrmann International teaches keeping a pad and pen at bedside to record dreams immediately after awakening. Otherwise, dreams are quickly forgotten. Once in hand, dreams can be interpreted relative to the problem on the person's mind the night before, as illustrated in the example below.

Collapsing Vacuum Hose

This example illustrates how a dream helped meet a need to creatively solve a difficult plant process problem that was taking a serious, costly toll on yields.

The creative dreamer was Floyd Ragsdale, an innovator in the Kevlar plant who had participated in on-site creativity workshops. Manufacturing was dealing with a process problem that was causing quality and cost problems. His account of the problem and creative solution follows:

> We had been fighting collapsing vacuum hoses in the Kevlar process for months. It was taking a tremendous toll on our yields. One day, I had been at the plant trying to find a solution for maybe 16 hours, and I needed some sleep. When I went home and got to bed, the problem throbbed in my head like a toothache, back and forth, back and forth.
>
> Eventually, I fell asleep. I started to dream, and in my dreams, I saw slinky toys, those spring-like coils that kids play with. I kept seeing these toy-like springs, over and over. I had been to a creativity workshop at the plant only a month before. One of the lessons was that we should pay attention to our dreams, because sometimes we have better insights when we relax and don't concentrate so hard. So I kept a pad and paper next to my bed. I came out of my dream and sat up. Still half asleep, I wrote on my pad: "Insert spring inside of vacuum hose, will correct problem."

Then I went back to sleep.

When I woke up at about 4:30 or 5:00 and headed into the plant, I took my paper with me. I saw the area supervisor and said, "We're in luck. I had a dream. Our problem is solved." He looked at me kind of funny, but I explained, and we ordered some customized stainless steel springs and inserted them in the hose. Doggone, that equipment started up running like a top and has been running well ever since.

Some people may wonder why the plant team had not thought about a spring sooner; it seemed so obvious. But most good ideas are obvious in hindsight. How often has someone come up with a good idea and you wondered why that hadn't been thought of before? It's like climbing a mountain and not seeing the best path up until reaching the top and looking down. It seems obvious in hindsight, but it wasn't while climbing that mountain.

Point of View

Challenging our point of view about an issue, an event, or a thing can jog our thinking outside normal patterns and can lead to entirely new ideas and concepts.

A technique taught by author Roger von Oech is to substitute your own thinking with the point of view of another person known for having a unique style of creative thinking.[29] The example below illustrates the application of this technique.

Cutting Through Red Tape

A business team was searching for needs-driven ideas on how to commercialize a product rapidly by cutting through administrative red tape. The technique that proved the most useful in this case was to view the problem from the point of view of Lee Iacocca, former CEO of Chrysler.

Someone in the group related a story he had heard about how Lee Iacocca had re-entered Chrysler in the convertible automobile market. At the time, convertibles had been out of style for years because of safety issues. Iacocca decided to test the public reaction to a convertible and asked the manufacturing manager how fast he could deliver a convertible to display. The response was that, if given high priority, it could be ready in 6 months. As the story goes, Iacocca turned red with anger. He ordered the manager to rip the roof off an existing car and have the convertible ready by the next morning.

This story lifted the business team to a more intensive plateau of creative thinking. There was a burst of aggressive, unorthodox ideas in tune with how Iacocca would address their problem, e.g., elimination of all paperwork. This session paid off and helped lay the basis of a fast-track program.

Dare to be Different

Mike Emery, Business Director at Tyvek®, promoted this point of view:

> Dare to be different.

His concept was that innovators would benefit from being willing to be different in a positive, constructive way. The only constraints were that the action be legal, moral, and safe. Below is an example that illustrates his approach and his willingness to practice what he preached.

A marketing representative in Emery's organization visited a customer to respond to a complaint. The representative concluded that the complaint was valid, took out his wallet, and paid the claim. He charged it on his expense account. The accountants yelled "foul," but Emery had a party to acknowledge the marketing representative's daring to be different, giving status to this act, and reinforcing the environment for creative thinking.

Fantasizing

A technique taught by Joyce Juntune, Director, Institute for Applied Creativity, Texas A&M University, and Morris Stein, Professor Emeritus, Psychology, New York University is to change a point of view about an object by first eying it analytically and then fantasizing.

For example, select a pencil and describe it from an analytical point of view. It might be round, yellow, eight inches long, have a grey lead point and a half-worn eraser. Now fantasize. I wish it could do the following: write by itself; be eaten; never wear out; sharpen itself; write in several colors; and illuminate the darkness.

Using this technique with a team of three or four innovative thinkers would likely generate, within 30 minutes, more than 100 ideas from which some could be selected to form the basis for a new line of pencils.

Capitalizing on the "Unexpected"

An unexpected result sometimes is ignored as a mistake or failure. At other times innovators with a "prepared" mind recognize that the unexpected happening might present an opportunity for an important innovation. This section describes two product innovations sparked by capitalizing on the unexpected.

Spunbonded Nonwoven Fabrics

This example illustrates how a major new business venture was born by a research engineer observing an unusual phenomenon that he associated with a need, triggering an idea to meet the need.

A research engineer at the DuPont Carothers Research Laboratory was exploring ways to spin a fuzzy nylon filament yarn. His approach was to blow short floc fibers against a molten spinning threadline to obtain hairlike projections. He couldn't get the floc fibers to stick, so he tried electrostatics. Normally the yarn is wound up on a bobbin, but the spinning operator was late in inserting the windup bobbin and the yarn fell to the floor. As it did so, the electrostatically charged fibers spread out into a sheetlike structure.

At the time, the mid-1950s, there was a need in the marketplace for low-cost nonwoven fabrics from synthetic fibers. The engineer was aware of this need. When he observed the fibers spreading into sheet structures on the floor, he realized that this was an entirely new concept in sheet structure formation. This observation ultimately led to DuPont's Reemay® and Typar® spunbonded, nonwoven fabric innovations.

Dye-Resistant New Styling Yarns

This example illustrates how a positive-thinking innovator interpreted an unexpected negative result in a positive way, resulting in a valuable product innovation.

A need existed for a more rapidly dyeable nylon carpet fiber. A research scientist took the approach to chemically modify the nylon polymer. In one experiment, the result was the opposite of what he expected or wanted. The fiber could not be dyed at all! But, instead of discarding this negative result, he took a positive view. He reasoned that he could mix this nondyeable fiber with dyeable fibers and get unique styling effects. This was the birth of dye-resistant styling yarns, which materialized into a profitable product in the nylon carpet line.

Many examples of how unexpected events led to innovations are described in the book *Corporate Creativity*.[30]

Focused-Thinking Framework

After using one of the six methods described above to generate new ideas, it is often useful to apply the Edward de Bono Six Thinking Hats framework discussed below to evaluate the new ideas critically as a next step. Another valuable approach for focused thinking is the three-step problem solving process described in Chapter 4.

The Six Thinking Hats

The Six Thinking Hats, designed by Dr. Edward de Bono, is an ingenious framework to think through a subject in a focused way that makes time and space for creative thinking.[7] It has been used extensively in companies such as DuPont, IBM, Prudential Life Insurance, British Airways, and Hewlett Packard as a way to have efficient, productive meetings, especially when dealing with complex, controversial issues where emotions run high. This framework is taught in de Bono Thinking Systems® training courses.[28]

The underlying principle in the Six Thinking Hats framework is that parallel thinking is more productive than argument. The six hats are shown below.

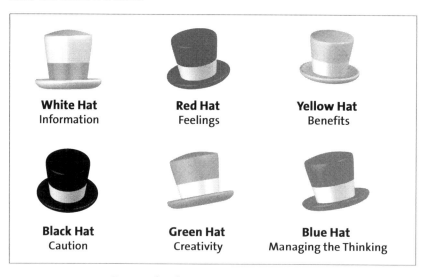

White Hat	Red Hat	Yellow Hat
Information	Feelings	Benefits

Black Hat	Green Hat	Blue Hat
Caution	Creativity	Managing the Thinking

Reprinted with permission. ©2012. I P Development Corporation.
Published by de Bono Thinking Systems®.

Each hat has a different color and represents a different dimension in thinking about the subject being addressed. The *White Hat* deals with information, the *Red Hat* with feelings, the *Yellow Hat* with benefits, the *Black Hat* with caution, the *Green Hat* with creative ideas, and the *Blue Hat* with thinking about managing the thinking. Everyone wears the same hat at the same time.

Hats can be put on and taken off depending on the sequence in thinking that makes the most sense. It's something like using a set of golf clubs. Each club has a different purpose and can be taken out and put back depending on the situation. Six Thinking Hats can be used individually or in groups, at work or at home. Each hat is described in more detail below.

White Hat Thinking

Think of paper or a computer printout. This hat deals with factual information. What information do we have? What information do we need? It provides background to the issue being addressed. It pinpoints action needed to fill gaps. Importantly, it separates fact from speculation. The following story illustrates this point in a humorous way:

> A man named Arnold was standing on a street corner with a dog at his side. A second man approaches and asks, "If I pet your dog, will your dog bite me?" Arnold replies, "My dog doesn't bite." So the man pets the dog and the dog bites him! He says, "I thought you said that your dog doesn't bite!" Arnold replies, "This isn't my dog."

Red Hat Thinking

Think of fire or warmth. The *Red Hat* deals with feelings, intuition, and emotions. It gives participants permission to express feelings. There is no need to justify or explain reasons. The *Red Hat* also covers "gut" feelings based on experience. In dealing with important issues at home or at work where a decision is required, we may collect much information related to the issue, but we usually make our final decision based on our gut feeling.

The *Red Hat* is often used during a creative thinking session to invite participants to express feelings about whether an idea should be implemented. A business meeting addressing a controversial issue might start out with each person wearing the *Red Hat* to express his or her feelings about the subject. This sometimes will change the meeting agenda.

Yellow Hat Thinking

Think of sunshine. This is the "positive thinking" hat. It relates to benefits, values, and the feasibility that an idea will work. When wearing this hat, everyone thinks positively. *Yellow Hat* thinking reinforces creative ideas, new directions. *Yellow Hat* thinking points need to be supported by logical reasons. Often the *Yellow Hat* is used early in a session to support benefits of an idea or concept. An important value of the *Yellow Hat* is that even people opposed to an idea are forced to think positively and may be stimulated to contribute creative benefits.

Black Hat Thinking

Think of a judge wearing a black robe. This hat deals with judgment, caution, difficulties, risks. It is a valuable, necessary, and very important hat. It prevents false starts and silly mistakes. It pinpoints weaknesses and impracticalities. But overusing the *Black Hat* creates a serious problem. Critical thinking about an idea comes very naturally to most people, so it is not uncommon for overuse of *Black Hat* thinking to be a problem.

Green Hat Thinking

Think of vegetation, growth, and energy. This is the creative hat, used to generate new ideas and possibilities and to explore alternate courses of action. Wearing the *Green Hat* provides the opportunity to think creatively about how to gain the benefits of a good idea while overcoming barriers. *Green Hat* thinking is catalyzed by creativity tools such as lateral thinking.

Blue Hat Thinking

Think of a blue sky or an overview. This hat manages the thinking process. When participants wear the *Blue Hat*, they are thinking about thinking, e.g., what sequence of hats makes most sense in dealing with the issue. This hat is also involved with process control. The person leading the session often has to remind people which hat is being worn. When the group is wearing the *Yellow Hat*, some folks might find it tempting to be critical of a benefit. The leader would then suggest postponing the criticism until the group wears the *Black Hat*. The *Blue Hat* is also worn when it is time to summarize output of the meeting.

Summary of the Focused-Thinking Framework

The Six Thinking Hats framework:

- Encourages parallel thinking with others
- Directs thinking in discrete segments
- Switches thinking from one mode to another
- Explores a subject more thoroughly
- Makes specific time and space for creative thinking
- Separates ego from performance
- Can be used individually or in groups

This has been a brief description of the Six Thinking Hats. Workshops are available to learn and practice this valuable framework in depth.[28] When dealing with an important issue affecting an organization, it's essential that an experienced, certified facilitator lead the process.

Applications

The Six Hats Framework can be used in a variety of ways:

- Evaluating and upgrading ideas and proposals
- Planning for implementation of an innovative idea
- Resolving controversial issues
- Generating new ideas and concepts

Resolving Controversial Issues

This example describes how the Six Thinking Hats framework helped settle a controversial technical issue that had stymied progress in development of a major new product innovation.

A West Coast high-technology company embarked upon an effort to develop a next-generation, bread-and-butter product. An engineering task force was formed that spent several weeks identifying three alternative approaches. However, progress was stymied because of disagreement on which of the three approaches to pursue. The task force badly needed to resolve this issue for the program to proceed.

The task force leader was familiar with the creative thinking field and hired an experienced facilitator to help resolve this problem. The Six Thinking Hats framework was ideal to lead the team through a focused-thinking session to evaluate and upgrade each approach.

As a first step, the Six Thinking Hats framework was reviewed. The team was then divided into three subgroups, each applying the Six Hats framework to evaluate and upgrade one of the three next-generation approaches.

Each team started with *Yellow Hat* thinking to define benefits and feasibility. *Black Hat* thinking defined barriers. *Green Hat* thinking generated creative ideas on how to overcome barriers, retain benefits, and upgrade the technical approach. *White Hat* thinking identified information needed to fill gaps in their knowledge.

At several points in the session, each team shared its Six Thinking Hats thinking with the entire group to benefit from each others' views. Particularly productive was the sharing of *Green Hat* ideas on ways to upgrade the technical concepts of each approach.

During the final hour of the session, *Red Hat* thinking gave participants the opportunity to share their feelings on which approach was best. Having thought through the issue in a focused way, there was unanimous agreement on which path had the most promise. An important benefit of this session was buy-in by all team members on which was the best path to pursue.

Focused Thinking About a Family Issue

My youngest son, Philip, was graduating college as a finance major and decided that, instead of looking for a job, he wanted to start his own business. He proposed purchasing a franchise business. What particularly caught my attention was that he wanted me to finance the venture. I suggested that we think this project through using the Six Thinking Hats framework, with which he was familiar.

Under the *White Hat*, my son described information he had about the franchise. Under this hat, I asked many questions to better understand the background and potential opportunity. In *Yellow Hat* thinking, he made many positive points about benefits. As I became acquainted with the prospects, I enthusiastically joined in with additional potential benefits. During *Black Hat* thinking, my wife became a valued member of the team. This was beneficial, since critical thinking comes easily for her.

In this session, the *White Hat* was quite valuable. Toward the end of the discussion, the family put this thinking hat back on and focused in parallel on what additional information would be needed before a decision would be made. This became the basis for action steps. Guess what the family used as the focal point in *Green Hat* thinking? "What alternatives are available to finance the venture?"

The entire session took close to an hour to think through the proposal, generate action steps, and gain buy-in of all concerned. The outcome was that I did finance the project which turned out to be very successful. My son paid me back within 1 year. He has several franchises, which provide good cash flow and enable him to spend much time on his first love, which is in the investment field.

Evaluating and Upgrading Ideas

This example describes how the Six Thinking Hats framework helped evaluate a controversial idea aimed at developing a portfolio of new products.

A research and development (R&D) planning team of the DuPont Industrial Products Division recommended to divisional management the formation of a new business that would capitalize on the combined strengths of the existing individual businesses of Kevlar, Nomex, Tyvek, Sontara®, and Teflon®.

The idea was controversial. Business managers felt it would dilute resources from their businesses and were strongly opposed. R&D management was strongly in favor. A 2-hour meeting was scheduled to evaluate this controversial idea. The meeting was designed based on the Six Thinking Hats framework. The business managers were agreeable since the division had an ongoing creative thinking program, and they were familiar with the value of this framework. The divisional facilitator led the session, supported by the divisional creativity manager.

The meeting started with a brief *White Hat* overview and discussion of the proposed idea. Then, instead of *Yellow Hat* thinking to elicit positive benefits, which is the usual sequence of hats, the facilitator initiated *Black Hat* thinking. An energetic discussion by business managers resulted in many hang charts listing serious difficulties with the idea. This allowed business managers to air reasons, many justified, why they were opposed.

Next was *Yellow Hat* thinking. There was dead silence. The R&D people purposely said nothing. Then one of the business managers noted a benefit. This started the ball rolling. Soon, all business managers joined in, and there were as many hang charts listing benefits as those containing difficulties.

Green Hat thinking generated many creative ideas on how to retain benefits while overcoming difficulties. Everyone was now energetically engaged in upgrading the idea to make it workable. The R&D planning team was charged to develop a stepwise implementation plan for further review, embodying the suggested changes. The business managers now had strong buy-in.

In subsequent meetings, agreement was reached on next steps. Many years later, a DuPont Safety & Protection business segment was formed that embodies many of the principles discussed in the Six Thinking Hats session.

Dealing with an Education Issue

David Campbell, district superintendent, Delaware school system, invited me to attend a monthly meeting of the six North Delaware school superintendents to discuss potential application of creative thinking knowledge in the education system.

I was invited to one of the superintendents' monthly meetings. Each superintendent was asked to write down the three most important issues he or she was dealing with personally. This caught their attention! As they each volunteered their issues, the issues were listed on the blackboard. After eliminating duplication, there were eight issues of primary interest. These were discussed, and the superintendents agreed that the most important issue pertinent to all of them was:

> How can we achieve third-grade reading competencies
> for all students upon completion of third grade?

They were all anxious to tackle this issue in a half-day creative thinking session and agreed to each bring with them three educators, including principals from their school. The half-day meeting was held to deal with the above issue, led by two experienced facilitators from the DuPont Center for Creativity & Innovation.

The group of 30 participants generated numerous ideas related to this issue, using various creativity tools. Convergent thinking led to selection of the three best ideas. The Six Thinking Hats framework was then applied to evaluate and upgrade these ideas. Each team shared its thinking with the whole group, which then voted on the best idea to consider implementing. The selected idea:

Teach parents how to teach reading in the home.

The concept behind the idea was that most parents play a key role in teaching their children how to talk, how to walk, and how to ride a bicycle. Why not teach parents how to teach children how to read? Some of the participants were enthusiastic about pursuing this idea.

At a later date, I was invited by a professor at Drexel University in Philadelphia, to introduce her class of PhD candidates in education to the creativity and innovation field. As part of the lecture, the class was introduced to the Six Thinking Hats.

To illustrate the practical value of this framework, the class of about 20 students was asked to evaluate the idea generated by the Delaware District Superintendent's meeting described above. The Six Hats approach allowed them to evaluate the idea in a focused way, but with intense differences of opinion while wearing the *Yellow* and *Black hats* multiple times and periodically putting on the *Green Hat*.

The scheduled 1-hour evening class lasted more than 3 hours without gaining unanimous agreement on whether this was a good idea for the education community to pursue. However, the professor sent me a note commenting that many of her students were so affected by the Six Thinking Hats process that it completely changed their approach to dealing with issues.

Reversing Opinion on an Important Proposal

This example describes how a corporate team applied the Six Thinking Hats process to the need to resolve a controversial proposal having important budget control implications. The result was to reverse initial thinking about the proposed idea.

A corporate advisory team of eight high-level members was formed to deal with an idea that had emerged from an executive strategic planning meeting. The idea was that all R&D directors in the company should submit a structured cost-benefit analysis on each of their major programs to help decide annual budget allocations.

Corporate team members looked favorably on the proposed idea and felt it should be implemented. R&D directors were strongly opposed, concerned that the implications had not been thought through carefully enough.

A 1-hour meeting was organized to resolve this controversial proposal. The group was familiar with the Six Thinking Hats process because of a corporate creativity and innovation program and decided to apply this framework to accomplish the task. An experienced facilitator from the DuPont Center for Creativity & Innovation was assigned to lead the session. He was delighted as he had been practicing the Six Thinking Hats framework for several weeks since taking a training workshop. Now was his chance to apply his learning to an important issue.

The meeting began with a brief review of the Six Thinking Hats. *White Hat* thinking provided time for discussion of the proposed idea. *Yellow Hat* thinking generated a long list of benefits. It appeared obvious that the idea should be implemented. However, it turned out otherwise. In *Black Hat* thinking many serious negatives emerged, such as credibility of cost-benefit assumptions. *Green Hat* thinking generated creative ideas for upgrading the idea to overcome obstacles, but none was convincing. *Red Hat* thinking enabled each participant to express feelings about the proposal. The corporate advisory team reversed their original thinking and decided against the proposal.

Harvesting Best Ideas

This example illustrates how the Six Thinking Hats process helped a food company harvest its best ideas for dealing with the need to increase speed of delivery of its product. It illustrates the step-wise process of applying the Six Thinking Hats to think through a practical opportunity.

The manager of a Midwestern food company, familiar with the creative thinking field, organized a session to develop ideas on how to improve competitive position in home delivery of the company's food products. An experienced facilitator led the meeting, attended by a team of 12 participants who generated many ideas using several creative thinking techniques. The ideas were posted on flip charts. From this list, the group selected the three ideas they perceived to be the best for further evaluation and up-grading. The final step was to harvest the best of these three ideas. The Six Thinking Hats provided a framework to think through each of the selected ideas in a focused way. The sequence began with *Yellow Hat* thinking to define benefits that helped reinforce the idea. *Black Hat* thinking focused attention on difficulties and barriers that would have to be overcome. *Green Hat* thinking led to creative ways to overcome barriers while maintaining benefits. *White Hat* thinking identified information needed to fill gaps in the knowledge base and to implement the idea.

This sequence was followed for each of the three ideas, enabling the team to gain a better understanding of each idea. Finally, each participant used the *Red Hat* to express feelings about which ideas to implement.

This 2-hour session provided the manager with three well-thought-through ideas to increase competitive position and helped him decide which one to pursue. Another benefit was team buy-in of the idea selected for implementation.

Health Care Innovations

When innovative health care teams are searching for ideas to meet a need, the creative thinking techniques described above, such as lateral thinking and metaphoric thinking, would be helpful in generating many ideas, some quite unusual.

The three health care innovations discussed below use two other well-known creative thinking techniques to generate ideas: storytelling and brainstorming.

Alzheimer's Patients Aided by Storytelling[31]

Summary of the Program

The Timeslips program uses group storytelling to enhance the lives of people with Alzheimer's disease and related dementia. When persons with Alzheimer's disease and related dementia reach the middle and/or end stages of their disease, they often have significant impairment in memory and language skills, which makes it difficult for them to interact with others or have a meaningful social life. The Timeslips program encourages these people to use their creativity and imagination to create a story with their peers in weekly group sessions. Two studies have shown that this program has had a positive impact on persons with Alzheimer's disease and related dementia, leading to enhanced verbal skills and provider reports of positive behavioral changes, increased communication and sociability, and less confusion.

The Need

Alzheimer's disease and related dementia affect millions of individuals, leading to severe limitations for which there are few therapeutic options. Most long-term care providers (which are home to 70% of Alzheimer's/dementia patients) assume that these people cannot be helped. However, evidence suggests that parts of their memory can be stimulated and that encouraging communication can delay progression of the disease. An innovative approach was needed to capitalize on this evidence.

The Needs-Driven Innovation

The innovative approach involves structured weekly group meetings led by trained facilitators to encourage persons with Alzheimer's disease and related dementia to use their creativity and imagination to create a story that can be shared with fellow residents and family members. A volunteer or staff member leads weekly group sessions with 6 to 12 persons with Alzheimer's disease and related dementia. The meeting follows a very structured format because such individuals' procedural memory is still intact. Participants, who are referred to as "storytellers," sit in a circle. Each meeting progresses as follows:

At the beginning of each group session, facilitators explain that the group is a safe place for storytellers to express themselves and that all responses will be woven into the story. Facilitators retell the story that was created the week before to reinforce the fact that participants still have the capacity to be creative and to combat those who say they do not. Retelling the story also reminds the storytellers of the structure of the group.

The facilitators share a staged photograph or illustration and ask the storytellers questions about what is happening in the picture. Facilitators are purposeful in the way they encourage participants to become storytellers, building on participant responses and using specially designed types of questions to further stimulate imagination. Facilitators record all storytellers' answers, including seemingly nonsensical ones, on a large sheet of newsprint in an attempt to capture the emotion of what was said. If a storyteller contributes a response that does not seem to make sense, the facilitator repeats the response to the storyteller to make sure that he or she has captured it properly. Responses are recorded and crafted into a story either chronologically or grouped by clusters.

Periodically, the facilitator rereads the story that the group has already created; the goal of this exercise is to keep participants engaged and to help them expand the story. When the group completes the story, the facilitator reads it back to them using the same emotion and enthusiasm that the storytellers themselves used. Once the story is completed, facilitators and storytellers celebrate what they have created by clapping, and the facilitators thank the storytellers for participating.

Results

Studies have shown that the Timeslips program has had a positive impact on persons with Alzheimer's disease and related dementia, leading to enhanced verbal skills and provider reports of positive behavioral changes, increased communication and sociability, and less confusion.

One study evaluated an 18-week program that was implemented in four adult day care centers. An analysis of the content of the stories found several common themes among participants, including humor and a clear desire for more freedom and human connection. In all four groups, storytellers engaged in the storytelling process as a method of self-expression.

Use by Other Organizations

Timeslips has 12 regional training bases across the country that are funded by a grant from The Commonwealth Fund. These training bases were developed to facilitate dissemination of the program throughout the nation.

Walk-In Health Care MinuteClinics[32]

Summary of the Program

The MinuteClinic operates walk-in primary care clinics located within retail stores. Staffed by nurse practitioners and physician assistants, these clinics use electronic health records and decision-support tools to provide low-cost, evidence-based primary care services, including the diagnosis and treatment of common illnesses and skin conditions and the administration of routine vaccinations. Patients are highly satisfied with the quality and convenience of services. Various studies suggest that clinic services cost less than similar services provided in other settings, and that they generally conform with evidence-based guidelines.

The Need

Rick Krieger was frustrated with the long wait and slow service he encountered when taking his son to an urgent care center for diagnosis and treatment of a sore throat. There was clearly a need for a way to accommodate people with faster health care service.

The Needs-Driven Innovation

To identify ways to meet the need, Krieger brought together a few key people including a local primary care doctor, a nurse practitioner, and an entrepreneur. They brainstormed ideas that led to the innovative concept of a retail health care clinic. The result was their commitment to the notion of using nurse practitioners as front-line providers offering easy access to a set of routine services.

The innovative concept evolved during a series of weekly meetings. Over time, this small diverse group began working with commercial real estate firms, venture capitalists, local regulators, and others to make the concept a reality.

Results

The first kiosk, entitled MinuteClinic, was erected in a ministorage warehouse in 1999. By the end of 1999, a kiosk opened in a local strip mall. In May 2000, MinuteClinic signed an agreement with Cubs Food Stores and opened the first MinuteClinic within a retail store. MinuteClinic, currently owned by CVS/Caremark, operates approximately 500 retail clinics in 24 states and the District of Columbia. Each clinic offers quick access to a focused set of services to walk-in patients over 18 months of age.

The MinuteClinic is staffed by nurse practitioners and physician assistants who use electronic health records and decision-support tools to provide low-cost, evidence-based primary care services. These include diagnosis and treatment of common illnesses and skin conditions and the administration of routine vaccinations. Patients are highly satisfied with the quality and convenience of services. Various studies suggest that clinic services cost less than similar services provided in the typical emergency department, urgent care center, or physician's office.

Use by Other Organizations

Retail clinics have been increasing nationwide according to Merchant Medicine. Walgreens operates 340 Take Care clinics nationwide. The Little Clinic operates in a variety of retail locations including grocery stores and home electronics stores in 11 states. Walmart and Target stores also have retail clinics at select locations.

Transforming Care at the Bedside[33]

Summary of the Program

As a pilot site for the Transforming Care at the Bedside initiative, Seton Northwest Hospital continuously designs and tests nurse-led quality improvement projects at the patient's bedside using a rapid-cycle improvement process, with projects designed to meet one of four objectives: care safety/reliability, teamwork/staff vitality, waste reduction, and patient-centeredness. The hospital has undertaken more than 120 quality initiatives to date, making nurse-led performance improvement a routine part of everyday operations on the units. The program has allowed nurses to be more efficient and spend more time with patients, reduced patient falls and nurse turnover, accelerated patient discharge, and yielded positive feedback from staff and patients.

The Need

Up to 90 percent of hospital errors result from poorly designed systems, clearly indicating a need for fundamental process redesign. But many hospitals have focused their redesign efforts on areas such as the emergency department and the intensive care unit, while ignoring the redesign of bedside care in medical and surgical units, where much of hospital care is delivered. In addition, nurses play a central role in ensuring quality of care and have firsthand knowledge of care inefficiencies that affect patient care and staff satisfaction. Thus, there is a clear need for nurse-led innovations to help streamline processes and free up more time for patient care.

The Needs-Driven Innovation

Seton Northwest Hospital is a pilot site for the Transforming Care at the Bedside initiative. The hospital continuously designs and tests nurse-led quality improvement innovations at the patient's bedside. The process for nurse-led innovative quality improvement is based on a rapid-cycle sequence that quickly tests, measures, and revises changes. A key step in the process is a planning phase in which team members brainstorm process improvement ideas and refine ideas with a view toward reaching the "ideal" process.

Process improvement teams of innovative staff nurses identify areas for improvement in their own units/departments, set priorities for action, and then implement a multiphase process to test ideas including prototype testing, pilot testing of the prototype on a larger scale, and adaptation of the idea following lessons learned during the pilot. Examples of the many innovations derived by this process are described below.

Previously, each of the 13 gynecology surgeons admitting postoperative patients to the unit used a unique, hand-written order form, causing inefficiencies for nurses and pharmacists, and creating patient safety issues due to problems with legibility. Now surgeons use a single order set that incorporates common elements and the most frequently used best practices from the original unique forms. The order set includes basic instructions for a patient's medications, laboratory work, and recommended activity level. This standardization has allowed the pharmacy to create a standard record for its computer system and eliminated the need for nurses to transcribe information from the individual written forms. The success of this innovation has led to a similar approach being used for orthopedic surgeons who perform total knee and total hip replacement procedures.

A fall-reduction initiative seeks to ensure that staff members quickly recognize patients at risk of falling and respond appropriately to them. Nurses use the Hendrich II Fall Risk Assessment Tool to determine each patient's fall risk score. High-risk patients receive red slipper socks to highlight their need for extra assistance. In addition, flags placed outside the rooms and signs posted on the doors alert nurses and others to high-risk patients. All fall-prevention tools come together in a single package so that nurses can easily access them once they identify a high-risk patient.

The unit experiences 15 to 20 new patient admissions daily. Previously, the unit was inundated with requests to take in new patients, with a scheduler in charge of bed placement calling each nurse every 2 hours to ask whether he or she could accept a new patient assignment. Now, magnetic nurse status boards continually advertise nurses' current workloads. The board uses color-coded magnetic dots to reflect work intensity for each nurse, with a red dot signifying that the nurse is exceptionally busy and cannot take a new patient; a yellow dot meaning the nurse is getting caught up on work and will soon be ready for new patients or work assignments; and a green dot signaling that the nurse is available to help colleagues or accept a new patient.

To avoid situations in which nurses must roam the unit looking for basic supplies or order supplies from the central supply department, the unit now stocks frequently used supplies (e.g., oxygen tubing, suction catheters, thermometers, syringes, blood pressure cuffs, patient gowns, and linens) in each patient room. As the budget allows, this equipment will be available in all rooms. Central supply department and housekeeping staff take responsibility for stocking the rooms.

The unit altered its scheduling process to ensure that patients receive care from fewer nurses over the course of their stay. Nurses are now assigned to the same group of rooms on the unit, thereby increasing the likelihood that they will assume care for the same patients on subsequent shifts.

Previously, nurses and patients were often unprepared for discharge even when the patient was clinically ready to leave the hospital. Under the new system, nurses ask physicians during their rounds about the expected date of discharge and about the clinical criteria that must be met before the patient can leave the hospital. This information allows the nurses to provide care with a view toward timely discharge, to complete all administrative tasks related to discharge ahead of time, to give patients and families the predicted discharge date in advance, and to offer timely discharge education to patients and family members.

Results

Data from Seton Northwest Hospital and other pilot sites suggest that this innovation program has allowed nurses and other care-givers to be more efficient and spend more time with patients, reduce falls and nurse turnover, accelerate patient discharge, and yield positive feedback from staff and patients.

Use by Other Organizations

Along with Seton Northwest Hospital, other Transforming Care at the Bedside pilot sites included Shadyside, part of the University of Pittsburgh Medical Center, and Kaiser Foundation Hospital in Roseville, CA, part of Kaiser Permanente. An expanded pilot phase, implemented from June 2004 to May 2006, included 13 additional hospitals. The Robert Wood Johnson Foundation has also given a grant of more than $1 million to the American Organization of Nurse Executives to spread the Transforming Care at the Bedside program to more than 50 hospitals across the country.

Chapter 6

Diversity in Thinking

Diversity in thinking strengthens potential for success in all endeavors.

While innovative thinking skills are important in successful problem solving and innovation, another essential ingredient is diversity in thinking. This is particularly important as teams are formed to move ahead with an innovator-driven health care innovation.

What would happen if everyone on a health care project team, in Congress, or on a board of education, had the same background and experience, held the same values, and possessed the same thinking preferences and styles? Certainly there would be a relaxed atmosphere, communication would be easy, and one would expect that decisionmaking would be quick and painless. The trouble is, quickly made decisions would yield only humdrum results.

Teams that include people with different points of view work in an atmosphere that comes alive. They work harder at true communication, and decisions that are made are infinitely better because a number of points of view were considered in reaching them. Diversity in thinking preferences and styles always leads to more innovative solutions in any group.

This chapter describes two frameworks that measure diversity in thinking, with practical examples: The Herrmann Brain Dominance Instrument® (HBDI®) that measures preferences, and the Michael Kirton Adaption-Innovation Inventory (KAI) that measures creativity styles. These are not the only methods for assessing and describing thinking styles; however, they can provide useful approaches for steering groups toward more respectful and collaborative dynamics.

The Herrmann Brain Dominance Instrument® (HBDI®)

Ned Herrmann, an artist, a physicist by training, and a former manager of Management Education at General Electric, is the father of the Herrmann Brain Dominance Instrument®.[8, 9] The instrument integrates the scientific study of the brain with the study of human development. This section summarizes the Herrmann Brain Dominance Instrument® (HBDI®) and its practical applications.

Herrmann writes:

> The brain is specialized—not just physically, but mentally as well. Its specialty modes can be organized into four separate and distinct quadrants—each with its own language, perceptions, values, gifts and ways of knowing and being. We are all unique composites of those differing modes according to our particular mix of mental preferences and avoidances.

HBDI® Assessment Theory

The basic concept of the Herrmann® model is a metaphor for the brain composed of four interactive quadrants, each representing a category of thinking preferences. Combined together, these four quadrants represent the Whole Brain® Thinking Model.

Whole Brain® Model

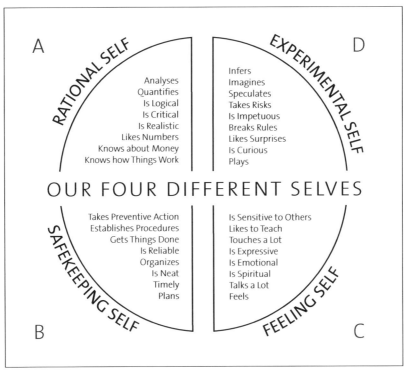

Many people with strong preferences in the upper left (A) quadrant prefer performing analytical, logical, and mathematical activities and tasks. In contrast, people with strong preferences in the upper right (D) quadrant prefer performing imaginative, intuitive, risky tasks and (or) activities. In other words, people with strong upper left (A) quadrant preferences may prefer to solve problems through reason and logic. People with strong upper right (D) quadrant preferences may prefer to think outside the norm, get flashes of ideas, and to brainstorm and speculate to solve problems.

The two lower quadrants are the focal points of the more visceral forms of mental processing. Structured, sequential, and organized mental activities are processed in the lower left quadrant of the brain (B). Emotional and interpersonal mental activities occur in the lower right quadrant (C). Taken together, the two cerebral hemispheres (A and D), and the two limbic hemispheres (B and C) form two different modes of thinking, which Ned Herrmann defines as our four different selves. For most of us, there is a brain dominance condition in which the quadrants work together, but with one or two taking the lead.

Measurement

The HBDI® Assessment has 120 questions that measures the degree of thinking preferences in each of the four quadrants.

Herrmann Brain Dominance Instrument® (HBDI®) Profile

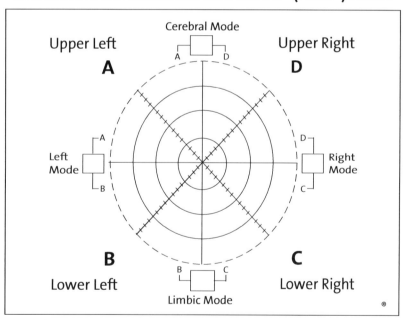

The 4-Quadrants Graphic is a registered trademark and copyright of Herrmann Global, LLC, and is reproduced with written permission for display in this text.
©Copyright 2012 Herrmann Global, LLC. All Rights Reserved.

Over a million men's and women's brain dominance profiles have been assessed by the HBDI® Assessment. The strong correlation between the HBDI® profile and human thinking preferences soundly validates the theory. Representative brain dominance profiles:

Representative Dominance Profiles

The 4-Quadrants Graphic is a registered trademark and copyright of Herrmann Global, LLC, and is reproduced with written permission for display in this text. ©Copyright 2012 Herrmann Global, LLC. All Rights Reserved.

Whole Brain® Thinking

Whole Brain® Thinking is particularly important in problem solving and dealing with difficult challenges. The HBDI® Profiles of members of a hospital staff are good examples. In hospitals, the doctors, nurses, administrators, and psychiatrists each often have different primary preferences.

Herrmann Brain Dominance Instrument® (HBDI®) Profiles

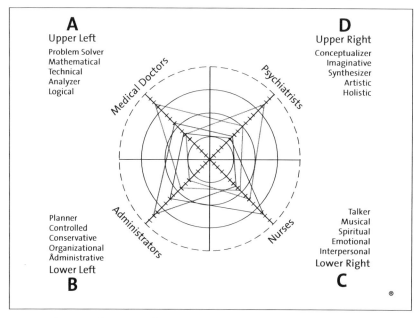

The 4-Quadrants Graphic is a registered trademark and copyright of Herrmann Global, LLC, and is reproduced with written permission for display in this text. ©Copyright 2012 Herrmann Global, LLC. All Rights Reserved.

The average profile HBDI® data in the graphic above shows that doctors often scored strong upper left (A) quadrant preferences, nurses often scored strong preferences in the lower right (C) quadrant, administrators often scored strong preferences in the lower left (B) quadrant, and psychiatrists often scored strong preferences in the upper left (D) quadrant. Each group generally forms cliques in the hospital environment. However, in an emergency, since each of these preferences is essential to success, tribalism is suppressed and all work together effectively as a Whole Brain® Thinking team.

Applications

There are many practical applications for the brain dominance concept, including the following:

- Interpersonal relationships
- Innovative problem solving
- Strategic planning team

Interpersonal Relationships

Understanding the concept of Whole Brain® Thinking and dominant quadrants is valuable in interpersonal relationships. It helps people to understand each other's thinking preferences and behaviors at work and at home.

Herrmann has described examples where marriages were saved by couples who took the HBDI® Assessment and subsequently understood each other's thinking. For example, a husband who is anxious to decide rapidly on buying a particular easy chair would normally be agitated by a wife who is meticulous about not making decisions until she does a thorough investigation of all factors. The HBDI® Profile helps him to understand that this is just her thinking preferences—that she is not agitating him on purpose.

Problem solving

The Herrmann Whole Brain® Thinking Workshop, was one of the most beneficial I had participated in during the period of being educated in the field of creative thinking and innovation. About 20 people with diverse backgrounds, including a corporate financial manager, an educator, a computer specialist, a journalist, a human resources manager, a self-employed entrepreneur, and a sculptor attended the session. All participants had taken the HBDI® Assessment in advance of the workshop but did not know results of their HBDI® Assessment until toward the end of the workshop.

Most of the workshop was devoted to problem solving in a variety of situations and in mixed groups. The most fascinating session occurred when three separate groups were formed and presented with the same problem. The only group that solved the problem had people with a mixture of thinking preferences in all four quadrants; hence, they tackled the problem with Whole Brain® Thinking.

Strategic Planning Team

The Tyvek business director had his staff take the HBDI®
Assessment to gain insights about the diversity of thinking in his
team. To his surprise, his core group of strategic planners, consisting of a marketing manager, a domestic strategist, an overseas
strategist, and himself had pronounced preferences, but supple-
mentary differences in their brain dominances. One had strong
preferences in the upper and lower left, A and B quadrants, another in the upper and lower right D and C quadrants, another in
the lower B and C quadrants.

Together, these four team members had strong preferences in all
four quadrants of the Whole Brain® Model. From that time on,
the director decided that he would not hold a strategic planning
meeting unless all four of them were present.

The Kirton Adaption-Innovation Inventory (KAI)*

Michael Kirton is a renowned British psychologist who pio-
neered The Kirton Adaption-Innovation Inventory (KAI).* He
related over dinner a delightful story of how, at the age of 7,
he observed that two relatives consistently behaved differently
when confronted with identical situations. This astute observation ultimately led to the widely applied KAI* that measures
people's creativity and problem solving styles.[10] This section
overviews the KAI and practical applications.

Basic Assumptions in the Adaption-Innovation Theory

- All people are creative; everyone generates ideas
  (novelty); everyone problem-solves.

- As far as brain operation is concerned, creativity
  and problem solving seem indistinguishable. The
  distinction may be little more than linguistic.

- Everyone is a change agent. This fits well into
  quality management where all are involved in
  quality operations.

---

* The Kirton Adaption-Innovation Inventory (KAI), KAI, and KAI Inventory are used
  with the permission of Dr. M. J. Kirton.

- Adaption-Innovation theory distinguishes sharply between style (what way) and level (how good). They do not correlate. Everyone can be measured on level: How creative am I? or style: How do I create?
- Level is related to skill, IQ, and competency, much of which can be improved by learning.
- Preferred style is unchanging throughout life, research shows. We can, however, learn to operate outside our preferred style by using coping behavior, when we acquire the insight that is needed.
- So, creativity is not always innovative or at high level.

The Adaption-Innovation theory postulates that people are creative and solve problems, to a greater or lesser degree, on a continuum of styles from *adaptive* to *innovative*.

The more *adaptive* prefer to make existing systems better; solve problems within existing paradigms; prefer a structured approach; are precise and dependable; and bring order and stability into novelty.

The more *innovative* prefer to make existing systems different; solve problems with less resolve to existing paradigms; prefer an unstructured approach; may be unique and visionary– and risky.

A successful organization has a range of adaptors and innovators. Both can generate novelty. The former does it within the system, the latter with less regard to current practice, policy, systems, and paradigms. Everyone, regardless of where they fall on the Adaption-Innovation range, is liable to produce a new product.

The adaptor's product is more likely to be an improvement on an existing general model—doing the job better. The innovator's product is more likely to be radical—doing it differently. However, they all need one another. For instance, a highly innovative new product will undoubtedly need further development, especially from adaptors, who will strive to make it more practical and more cost effective. Most people are not at the extreme of either direction in the continuum but have a preference in one direction or the other.

Adaptors often view innovators as unsound, impractical, and a source of confusion, even if they are stimulating and challenging. Innovators view adaptors as conforming, timid, and stuck in a "rut," even if they are dependable, sound, and expert in detail.

A person's creative-thinking style is stable and related to personality. However, behavior is flexible. The ability to shift style under circumstances where shifts are desirable is termed coping. Some people are better able to cope than others, having acquired the insight that it is needed and learned how to do so. Understanding the Adaption-Innovation theory generally helps people to become more conscious of the need to cope, particularly to other styles in a team situation. They realize that the primary focus is to solve the problem with the help of others on the continuum rather than despite them.

Excluding Dr. Kirton's own work, scholars have written some 350 journal articles and over 100 theses using the KAI theory and inventory. This research comes from several countries.

Measurement

KAI, as a measure of the theory, is a meticulously researched psychometric inventory that yields a score that distinguishes the more adaptive from the more innovative on a continuum.

Styles of Creativity

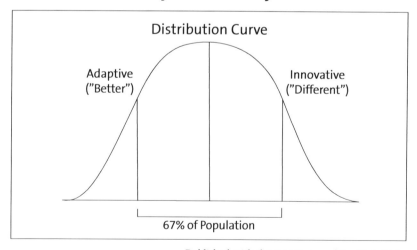

Published with the permission of Dr. M. J. Kirton.

In filling out the KAI Inventory,* consisting of 33 items, there are no right or wrong answers. Preference for a more adaptive or a more innovative approach to problem solving is not good or bad. Each has its own contribution in dealing with an issue. To obtain valid results, it is particularly important that answers represent how the person views himself or herself to be—not as he or she wants to be, or wants others to perceive him or her to be.

A purpose of the KAI is to help individuals understand their own and other people's preferences and behavior patterns. This aids relationships and performance.

The KAI effective range is just over 100 points. People who know each other well can likely detect a 10-point difference in their scores. A difference of 20 points might lead to conflict and discomfort. Larger differences might lead to serious communication problems. Understanding others' differences leads to admiration and respect. Those who have an intermediate KAI score within any mixed team have potential to act as active "bridgers" as long as they are willing and have learned the needed skills.

Relationship of KAI and Six Thinking Hats Framework

The Six Thinking Hats framework, discussed in Chapter 5, Innovative Thinking Techniques, generally works best with a mixed group of participants who range, in KAI terms, from highly adaptive to highly innovative.

Regardless of the hat the group is wearing, a mixed group of adaptors and innovators provides a more balanced input to the thinking process. For example, in Yellow Hat thinking on a proposal, adaptors generally contribute important thoughts on the more obvious benefits, while innovators consider the proposal from different angles, contributing thoughts on less obvious benefits.

In Green Hat thinking, innovators generate more unusual ideas and concepts, while adaptors contribute ideas that are seen as more immediately acceptable. In Blue Hat thinking, adaptors

---

* The Kirton Adaption-Innovation Inventory (KAI), KAI, and KAI Inventory are used with the permission of Dr. M. J. Kirton.

are more comfortable and likely to be the ones to summarize the output of the session in an orderly way.

During the six hat discussion, the adaptors consistently follow the rules of parallel thinking, while the innovators often stray and require reminders. Generally, adaptors and innovators contribute equally to the successful output of the session.

Applications

There are numerous situations where practical application of KAI is of value, including the following:

- Problem solving and coping
- Structuring a team; and
- Resourcing a task force.

Problem Solving and Coping

In organizing a problem solving workshop, it's beneficial to run a KAI on potential participants in advance of the event. This helps form teams with a good balance of thinking styles. The best balance may differ depending on the nature of the problem or opportunity being addressed. However, even ideal teams need to learn efficient coping behavior to be sure to manage problems not requiring the preferred style (and favored capacities).

Structuring a Team

I once consulted with a team of nine individuals who had been selected from various locations across the company to initiate a creative thinking and innovation program. The evening before the meeting, KAI theory was explained. Each participant was given a KAI inventory, which each filled out, and it was scored overnight.

The morning involved much interactive discussion. After lunch, each individual's KAI feedback booklet was given to each respondent as his or her private property. They were also given a chart of the spread of scores so they then saw the distribution curve showing that eight of them were in the continuum of being highly innovative. Only one in the group was in the adaptive category. In the morning session, this person had been ignored in most of the interactive discussion. They agreed to share each others' KAI scores and learned which one was the lone adaptive person.

The afternoon's session took quite a different turn from the morning session. The team showed a great deal of respect for the adaptor and listened carefully whenever he had something to say in the interactive discussion. This team would likely have benefited if more than one adaptive thinker had been on the team.

Resourcing a Task Force

A senior executive was in the process of resourcing a task force to implement an important facet of an innovation-oriented strategic plan. He had heard about the KAI in a creative thinking seminar and requested that a KAI be run on his total organization to provide insights on selection of task force members.

The KAI showed that his organization was biased in the direction of adaptor, which he felt was generally appropriate for his business and consistent with his thinking style. However, there were a few individuals whose styles were innovative, relative to the rest. Recognizing the value of diversity in thinking styles, this helped guide him in selection of task force members, some of whom had been identified as more innovative according to the KAI.

Other Applications

Those familiar with KAI theory who take into account thinking styles of the organization leadership are in a better position to sell their ideas and gain financial support and other resources helpful in pursuing their initiative or innovation, whether adaptive or innovative. This is also of value as the leader forms teams, adaptive, innovative or mixed as needed, and interacts with supporters, adversaries, and recipients of the initiative.

Leaders familiar with KAI are conscious of the diversity of thinking styles in their staff group and act as a bridge, particularly in dealing with controversial issues. Sales people familiar with KAI theory might often plan a sales pitch based on their perception of the customer's thinking style. A salesperson having an extreme innovator style would have trouble making the sale to a customer having an adaptor bias or vice versa, unless the salesperson was able to cope with the situation and organize the pitch accordingly.

Educators familiar with KAI are conscious of the importance of organizing their lessons in a way that appeals to both the more adaptive and the more innovative students. The same is true of seminar speakers familiar with KAI who organize their presentations in a way that appeals to a mixture of adaptor and innovator audiences.

Readers of this book who want to gain further information about the KAI should view Dr. Kirton's web site: www.kaicentre.com. This contains information about a four and a half-day KAI certification course, run since 1998. A team in Pennsylvania State University, the leading teaching center in the United States of this work, has set this course into a 9-credit, higher degree module. The web site also provides information about Dr. Kirton's textbook and latest publications.

The Wider Perspectives of Dr. Kirton's Theory of Problem Solving

The following paragraphs by Dr. Kirton are pertinent to the topic of this chapter and provide added perspective to the contents of this book.

The theory within which KAI is a style measure is that of problem solving. The brain developed in order to acquire what is needed to survive. It has the awareness to find (or create) within the environment opportunities to get what is needed and to manage (or avoid) what is hostile. It sets up the problem solving process from understanding the problem to finding and applying an appropriate solution and exploiting the outcome to achieve further success. This process (and others, i.e., creativity; invention) requires motive (the drive) to set it going in the right direction, at an adequate level, for the appropriate duration to complete the task. These cognitive elements constitute the strategy. The principal means are the appropriate capacities, each also at the appropriate levels (how good) and the appropriate style (in what way) needed to get the required solution to the specific current problem. This assumes, of course, that no specific capacity (or specific set of capacities) nor one specific style, at any one time during this problem solving process can always be the means of solving every problem. This need to continually select the appropriate means to solve a diversity of problems is one of the key learning needs of the brain, if it is to survive. When the brain has not the motive (often supported by collaborating emotion) backed by the appropriate levels and style, it has to learn how to acquire them and how to use them effectively, with the brain limits inherited.

Science is the highest means of acquiring the development of the needs to solve the problems that need solution. We must always be learning, as this book makes clear. Amongst this learning, then is that whatever solves one problem (or part of any complex problem) may not solve every other problem or every part of a complex problem. Yet our tendency is to believe that our existing knowledge (with modification) and our preferred style (with some flexibility) is the "best" start for every problem. But complex problems so often need a diversity of problem solvers, commanding between them the range of capacities and styles needed to solve this current specific common problem. That requires each member of the team, and particularly its leaders, to learn to arrange collaboration to make best use of their diversity to solve this particular common problem (called Problem A). Unfortunately, managing people not like us is not easy and requires more personal cost. So, the very diversity available to solve the problem may be the very diversity that pulls the team apart. It now becomes clearer that in (say) an engineering or finance problem, neither engineering nor finance, or even both, is likely to be enough). Equally, in a complex problem or a set of problems, is either adaption or innovation likely to be enough.

Capacities we usually understand better than styles. Adaption-innovation is a range on the one hand preferring solving problems by first setting each one into a consensually conceived paradigm and using approved methods to resolve them. Adaptors, then, bring about change as an outcome of solving the problem. Their weakness is that if the current paradigm does not contain the answer they either need more innovative colleagues and (or) some learning and coping behavior to re-set the boundaries of the perceived problem. Innovators are at their best when the problem needs re-setting, so they bring about change in order to solve problems. Their weakness is that when the answer lies within the tight structure of the current, consensually agreed paradigm (like a new element in the Periodic Table – a Nobel Prize-level problem) they find it more difficult to stay within it. Here is where they need those more adaptive, and to undertake more coping and learning.

In short, the Paradox of Structure is that all structure, including cognitive ones, can be enabling and simultaneously limiting. The limits help enabling when the structure is appropriate and limits tend to block change when different enabling is needed. So, the lesson offered by this theory is that we need to manage team diversity (i.e., those not like us), at the extra cost as that might be, in order to manage a diversity of problems to the reward of all within the team. Unwillingness to mange such diversities (Problem B) is the cause of many a team split and subsequent failure. Once we can manage the diversity of others, then our specialized expertise (e.g., innovation) can be put to powerful, collaborating use, just as this book suggests.

Health Care Innovations

This chapter described how people differ functionally in their style of thinking while participating in problem solving sessions and when implementing innovative ideas. Hence, diversity in thinking is vital when teams undertake difficult needs-driven innovations.

The innovations described below illustrate how hospitals use multifunctional teams in implementing innovations to capitalize on the different backgrounds and experiences of the involved individuals, who will likely have different patterns of thinking during problem solving.

Hospital Safety Culture [34]

This innovation punctuates the importance of multifunctional teams in implementing a program to enhance hospital safety culture. The importance of a culture for hospital safety is also discussed in the next chapter.

Summary of the Program

An innovative safety culture program was initiated at the Johns Hopkins Hospital, entitled the Comprehensive Unit-Based Safety Program (CUSP). An attending intensivist, Dr. Peter Pronovost, was the innovator and served as the primary catalyst for the program designed to accomplish the following: create partnerships between units and hospital executives to improve organizational culture; educate and improve awareness about patient safety and quality of care; empower staff to take charge and improve safety in the workplace; provide resources for unit improvement efforts; and provide tools to investigate and learn from defects.

The Need

Dr. Peter Pronovost, an attending intensivist, recognized the need to improve safety culture at the Johns Hopkins Hospital. He designed a program entitled CUSP.

The Needs-Driven Innovation

A unit-based team uses a structured process integrated into an organizational strategic plan.

Each unit forms an improvement team consisting of at least a physician, nurse, and the hospital executive. Ideally, teams are multidisciplinary in nature and include as many clinical disciplines as possible that work on the unit. Thus, respiratory therapists, pharmacists, and other staff members are encouraged to join the teams.

A Culture Checkup tool is used to structure group discussions within a unit around its culture assessment results and to help the team identify and work on any component (e.g., poor collaboration between physicians and nurses) that has weakened the culture. The Culture Checkup sparks an open dialogue about the culture of safety, providing a safe venue in which to discuss and resolve problems.

Safety culture is assessed using the Safety Attitudes Survey derived from aviation's Safety Climate Survey. Results from the baseline and ongoing safety culture assessments, sentinel events, and incident reports are shared periodically with the improvement teams and senior executives to stimulate discussion on how culture may pose a risk to safety and how these risks can be reduced.

Results

A pre- and post-implementation evaluation of CUSP in two surgical intensive care units at the Johns Hopkins Hospital found that the program improved the safety culture of the units and was associated with a reduction in intensive care unit (ICU) length of stay, medication errors, and possibly nursing turnover. The success on these units led to the decision to roll the program out to other units and clinical areas throughout the hospital, where safety culture has also improved. The CUSP program has also been implemented in Michigan ICUs, where it has led to improvements in culture.

Use by Other Organizations

The program has been rolled out in 170 clinical areas at the Johns Hopkins Hospital, and is being used in a national program in which it is combined with an intervention to reduce or eliminate central-line-associated bloodstream infections (BSI). This national program, called On the CUSP: Stop BSI, includes all 50 states, the District of Columbia and Puerto Rico, and also Spain and England.

Mobile Urgent Treatment Team[35]

This health care innovation example illustrates the importance of a multidisciplinary team offering diversity in thinking when dealing with complex emergencies.

Summary of the Program

The Mobile Urgent Treatment Team (MUTT) is a multidisciplinary team that provides 24-hour crisis intervention services to families in the Milwaukee area. MUTT defuses crisis situations and helps to find community services for the child and family as an alternative to institutionalization. The program, which is popular among both police and parents, has significantly reduced the need for hospitalization for children and adolescents after a crisis situation.

The Need

WrapAround Milwaukee is a county-run managed care organization that focuses on serving children and adolescents with complex mental health and emotional disorders. Staff went into the community to meet with key stakeholders including families, community agencies, and schools to determine their needs with respect to caring for these children. Staff also examined hospitalizations to determine the areas of greatest need.

The Needs-Driven Innovation

WrapAround Milwaukee staff canvassed the community to see what resources were available and then developed partnerships with these organizations. This led to the MUTT, a multidisciplinary team that provides 24-hour crisis intervention services to families in the Milwaukee area who have children with complex needs.

The MUTT team consists of 2 psychologists, 18 master's level crisis clinicians, social workers, case managers, a psychiatric nurse, and a psychiatrist on call for consultation. The team also provides services to families not enrolled in WrapAround when a child's crisis threatens removal from home or school. WrapAround began from a Federal grant to develop more comprehensive, community-based care for children with serious emotional needs and their families.

Results

MUTT has significantly reduced the use and costs of inpatient psychiatric facilities for children with complex needs who face a crisis situation; both police and parents are satisfied with the program.

Use by Other Organizations

MUTT and WrapAround Milwaukee have been in contact with other counties across the United States to help implement similar programs. The innovator, Dr. Chris Morano, now serves as the consultant to the newly formed mobile crisis team in Erie County, NY, called CARES. The CARES team has served families in the Buffalo, NY area since July 2009 and adopted much of the philosophy and strategies of MUTT. Other communities, including Chautauqua County, NY and Saginaw, MI are in the development phase of similar teams.

Medication Control for the Elderly[36]

This innovation illustrates the importance of a multifunctional caring team of health care professionals in administering an innovative computerized risk assessment screening system that improves health care of elderly patients.

Summary of the Program

Home health nurses and care managers use software-based protocols to screen older clients' medications and collaborate with pharmacists and physicians to reduce the risk of medication errors and adverse effects. The program identified and addressed many medication problems, leading to fewer cases of therapeutic duplication and more appropriate medication use overall and cardiovascular medications in particular.

The Need

Many community-dwelling seniors take multiple medications, putting them at risk for adverse events and medication errors. Frail seniors who use home health care services and Medicaid waiver programs may be at especially high risk, as these clients typically have multiple conditions and are cared for by a variety of doctors, nurses, pharmacists, and family members. Medication reviews can potentially reduce these risks, but they tend to occur primarily in institutional, not community, settings. Thus, there was an important need to establish innovative procedures to help protect frail seniors.

The Needs-Driven Innovation

An innovative approach to solve this problem was use of a computerized risk assessment screening system. Home health nurses and care managers collect health information from the client, including vital signs and other clinical indicators such as falls, dizziness, confusion, and medication use. The care manager or nurse enters the client's clinical information and medication list into the computerized risk assessment screening system.

The software alerts the user to potential medication problems using criteria developed by an expert panel. Based on the client's medication list and clinical indicators, the software identifies three types of medication problems common among frail, community-dwelling seniors: unnecessary duplication; signs of possible cardiovascular medication problems; and inappropriate use of anxiolytics, antidepressants, sleep aids, other psychotropic drugs and non-steroidal anti-inflammatory drugs (NSAIDS).

The nurse/care manager reviews the medication alerts with the patient in-home, follows up with the patient to verify the medication's dose and frequency as actually taken by the client, and updates the medication list if necessary.

The nurse/care manager contacts a consulting geriatric care pharmacist, asking for review of the client's clinical information and medication list. The pharmacist may access the software directly or may request a faxed profile or information via email. The pharmacist verifies the regimen's appropriateness, identifies problems or concerns that warrant evaluation by the physician, and develops recommendations for medication changes as appropriate. The pharmacist notifies the physician by faxed letter or by telephone in more critical situations. The physician reviews the patient's information and the pharmacist's recommendations, making changes to the medication regimen if appropriate.

Results

Both external evaluations of the program, a randomized controlled trial by Vanderbilt University in home health programs, and a followup prepost study by the University of Southern California in Medicaid waiver programs found substantial and significant improvement in medication use. Both rounds of implementation identified and addressed several common medication problems found among older adults, leading to fewer cases of therapeutic duplication and more appropriate medication use overall.

Use by Other Organizations

The program has been adopted by home health agencies, Medicaid waiver programs, Area Agencies on Aging, hospital transitions programs, and preventive health programs in California, Florida, Illinois, Minnesota, Texas, and Wisconsin. Organizations interested in adopting the program can contact the Partners in Care Foundation to schedule an on-site consultation.

Chapter 7

Promoting an Innovative Culture

An innovative culture in health care systems such as hospitals, medical groups, nursing homes, and community clinics supports the development and spread of innovative ideas. To create an innovative culture, it's necessary to create a supportive environment and to educate employees in the skills of innovative thinking and innovation. This chapter tells how this was accomplished in the DuPont Industrial Products Division, a group of seven businesses including Kevlar, Nomex, Tyvek, and nylon. It then describes the results at several innovative health care organizations.

In the mid-1980s, the DuPont Industrial Products Division was under severe competitive pressure. It had strong programs on TQM—Total Quality Management—but so did everyone else. To maintain a strong competitive position there was a need, in addition to TQM programs, to generate entirely new ideas and concepts. To accomplish this, it was necessary to create an innovative culture. Hence, steps were taken to enhance the environment for creative thinking and innovation and to educate employees in the skills of creative thinking.

Importance of a Supportive Environment

A supportive work environment for innovative thinking and innovation is a key component in an organization striving to promote an innovative culture. A symposium in 1986, sponsored by the Center for Creative Leadership, headquartered in Greensboro, NC, had a series of speakers discussing the importance of work environment. A summary of thinking that emerged at this symposium provided the following insight regarding impact of work environment on people's innovative behavior:

> It's insufficient for an organization to have creative, innovative individuals. The environment must be structured for creative tension, positive turbulence around a vision, and the space and freedom for people to "dance with their ideas" without fear of mistakes.

The impact of environment on people's behavior is vividly illustrated by the experiment described below. It was organized by the Washington Post as part of a social experiment about perception, taste, and people's priorities. In this experiment, the people were in such a hurried environment that they disregarded an event in the surroundings which ordinarily would have been of high interest and value. It punctuates the importance of an organizational culture where a hurried environment does not impede people's opportunity to observe events in their surroundings which might have value in influencing future innovations. An innovative environment is one where people have time and space to think and work innovatively.

The Washington Post Experiment

In a Washington, DC Metro station on a cold January day in 2007, a man with a violin played six Bach pieces for about 45 minutes. During that time approximately 2,000 people went through the station, most of them on their way to work. After about 3 minutes, a middle-aged man noticed there was a musician playing. He slowed his pace and stopped for a few seconds and then hurried to meet his schedule. Four minutes later the violinist received his first dollar from a woman who threw the money into the hat and, without stopping, continued to walk. Six minutes later a young man leaned against the wall to listen to him, then looked at his watch and started to walk again. After 10 minutes, a 3-year old boy stopped, but his mother tugged him along hurriedly. This action was repeated by several other children but every parent, without exception, forced the child to move on quickly.

For 45 minutes the musician played continuously. Only 6 people stopped and listened for a short while. About 20 gave money but continued to walk at their normal pace. The man collected a total of $32. After 1 hour he finished playing and silence took over. No one noticed. No one applauded nor was there any recognition.

No one knew this, but the violinist was Joshua Bell, one of the greatest musicians in the world. He played one of the most intricate pieces ever written, with a violin worth $3.5 million. Two days before, Joshua Bell sold out a theater in Boston, where the seats averaged $100.

If this experiment had been held in a less hurried environment, such as a city park or a vacation beach, the outcome would likely have been quite different.

Innovative Culture Program

The challenge of initiating a program to create an innovative culture, bolstered by a supportive environment for creative thinking and innovation, is difficult. Human nature is to resist change, resist "another program" on top of current assignments. Announcement of a new program is often regarded as just another whim of current management. This would certainly be the case in an attempt to initiate a creativity and innovation program.

We decided to proceed with such a program, but in a way that would avoid the usual inertia. The approach taken was not to announce a creativity and innovation program, but to just start doing certain things. An action-oriented culture-change model, designed by a DuPont consultant, was adapted to help achieve our goal of an innovative culture.

Culture Change Model

A culture can be defined by the four components, shown below, and changed by shifting these components:

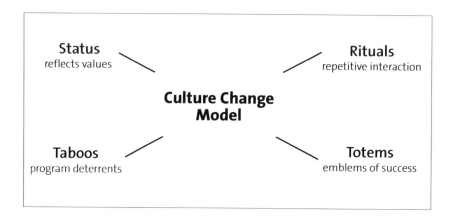

A. Status

Status is where we are grounded. Giving status to an effort reflects what management values. Technical unit heads gave status to the effort by occasionally substituting monthly day-long program reviews with skill-building creativity seminars and workshops. The substitution emphasized the workshops' significance. In the morning there would be a guest speaker, like Edward de Bono, teaching lateral thinking techniques. In the afternoon, three to four cross-functional teams, working on real problems, would apply what they learned in the morning session.

This approach enabled people to experience in a practical way the value of innovative thinking tools. It gave tremendous status to the effort. It began the education process. Site libraries stocked books on creativity and innovation. People began requesting attendance at external workshops and seminars. Innovator champions began to emerge and apply innovative thinking tools in their jobs. The "unannounced program" was underway.

The occasional substitution of technical program reviews with creativity and innovation workshops was the first step in giving status to the creativity and innovation effort.

Another step in giving status to the effort was involvement beyond research and development (R&D) of the marketing, manufacturing, and business functions. All functional directors met to discuss ways to apply creative thinking tools across the division. This led to formulation of a vision:

- Creativity and innovation are valued at all levels in the organization, and management behavior consistently signals and reinforces this value.

- Employees are knowledgeable about the technology of creative thinking and innovation and are applying the skills they develop.

- Employees have the space and take the time to be more creative and innovative.

Multifunctional teams were formed to implement the vision.

Further status was gained by appointing a divisional creativity manager who became thoroughly versed in creative thinking techniques by attending many seminars and workshops. He communicated knowledge in the field of creative thinking and innovation and cofacilitated creative problem solving sessions with the divisional facilitator.

B. Rituals

Many repetitive interactions were initiated by management and site innovator champions to help foster an innovative culture. These included the following:

- Creativity social hours
- Green Hat creativity hours
- Principles of Effective Thinking workshop
- Creativity and Innovation newsletters
- Special events

Creativity Social Hours

An effective way to cascade creative thinking awareness in the organization was to hold Creativity Social Hours during monthly visits of management to R&D technical unit sites. These coffee-and-cake sessions were held at the end of the day following program reviews. Before the visit, each unit head was requested to invite two or three individuals in the unit to speak about a creative idea they had thought of in their program and were implementing.

This ritual stimulated the unit head to think about who in the organization was doing creative work that merited recognition. What was the first thing he would ask his group managers in his weekly staff meeting? Who in your group has been doing creative work lately? This had the effect of cascading through the management line an increased awareness and interest in creative work being done in his group.

The highlight of these Creativity Social Hours was the enthusiasm with which each speaker described his or her creative idea and how it was being implemented. It didn't matter whether he or she used a specific creativity technique. The main point was that each took the time to think about creative alternatives to help solve problems or seek new opportunities. Over a period of years, everyone invited to speak agreed to do so. People love to talk about their work.

Asking people to be creative is like asking a child to be good. They don't know what you mean. But, hearing a colleague describe how creative thinking helped in his or her work gave meaning to creativity. The metaphoric thinking example described in Chapter V, Innovative Thinking Techniques, that led to a dyeable Nomex fiber innovation, was first aired in one of these Creativity Social Hours.

Engineers in the plant process units originally felt that creative thinking was mainly of value to research people. This changed when they heard a fellow engineer describe how a creative idea helped him increase productivity of a manufacturing process under development by 20 percent versus the goal of only 5 percent. They now understood what was meant by creative thinking and how it might benefit them. Hence, they became more involved in the unit's creativity effort.

Green Hat Creativity Hour

Several units had periodic creative problem solving sessions to apply and practice creative thinking to issues needing a new line of thinking. One such group was the industrial nylon R&D unit at the Chattanooga nylon plant. They had been active participants in the creativity and innovation effort and initiated a monthly Green Hat Creativity Hour. Their approach was to tackle difficult technical and manufacturing problems presented by colleagues, by applying the Six Thinking Hats framework which de Bono had taught in a plant workshop.

Their creative thinking session would start with Green Hat generation of ideas to solve a problem presented by a colleague, using lateral thinking, and then evaluate the best ideas using the Six Thinking Hats. In this way, they not only applied the techniques in group problem solving, but also gained experience for future use. One example was to apply the process to create new concepts for collecting and stabilizing a new fiber under development.

Principles of Effective Thinking (POET) Workshop

One of the most effective rituals in the program to create an innovative culture was a POET workshop, organized by innovator champion Jean Prideaux, a technical group manager for Kevlar Technical, with the help of several consultants.

The workshop was a hands-on, interactive experience that offered the opportunity to learn and practice creative thinking skills using the creative problem solving process. Participants worked on real problems and opportunities they brought to the workshop, which was attended not only by R&D people, but also by technicians, plant operators, and managers.

In one session, a team of technical engineers described a dead-end they had run into in scaling up a new Kevlar process that had been demonstrated in the laboratory. The stake in succeeding with this new process was $30 million. They were ready to give up but, as a last resort, attended one of these meetings, seeking help to solve this problem. Many ideas were generated using a variety of creativity techniques. The result was an elegant idea worth testing. It worked, and the development proceeded enabling scale-up of the proprietary technology developed in the laboratory.

Creativity and Innovation Newsletter

A Creativity and Innovation newsletter was issued biweekly by the divisional creativity manager, Alex De Dominicis, who helped expand knowledge in the field. The newsletter was based on various sources and emailed to all divisional personnel and numerous others who were part of a creativity network across the company. An example is the "Honey Pot" story told in Chapter 2.

Special Events

The Richmond, VA plant site, which had Plant Technical units in Kevlar, Nomex, Tyvek, Teflon and industrial nylon, had an annual December creativity seminar/buffet to which all site technical and support employees were invited. The most successful of these had as the speaker, Dr. Annette Goodheart, a psychotherapist, who spoke about the connection between laughter and creativity.

When I stood up in front of an audience of about 200 and began to introduce her, Goodheart began laughing out loud! At first, we were all stunned. Then we realized that this was her way to shift from an apparently serious mood to one of fun.

Dr. Goodheart's main message was: "Take your job seriously, but yourself lightly." She told humorous stories about her huggable teddy bear. There was a lot of laughter. Miniature teddy bears were given to all 200 attendees. The following day, teddy bears showed up on many desks in the workplace as a reminder of the message.

C. Totems

Although totems are emblems of success that can be honored by reward and recognition, this is a controversial subject. Some believe that this causes jealousy and reduces communication among employees who feel others may use and get credit for their knowledge.

Our experience was that the benefits of reward and recognition outweigh potential negatives. We didn't wait until an idea reached commercial reality, but recognized and rewarded individuals and teams on the run when they generated novel ideas that were being successfully implemented in their programs. For example, in the Creativity Social Hours described above, innovators invited to describe their creative work were all smiles for the recognition. Following their presentations, they were given gift certificates for dinner for two in a local quality restaurant, which was much appreciated.

The "Golden Egg" Award

A story pertinent to the use of totems is about a "Golden Egg" award that was described in one of our creativity manager's newsletters. The award was created by a small group of company presidents who met once a month for a variety of reasons. They soon found out that a favorite part of their meeting was the sharing of mistakes and other misadventures. The enthusiasm members felt for these sharings led to the idea of a "Golden Egg" award. As one member put it, "I want to hear it from the member who got egg on his face trying out his idea." A trophy was soon put together (with the help of an egg-shaped pantyhose container and some gold spray paint).

Presentation of this award for the best mistake of the month became a standard part of their meeting, and the trophy added an important new dimension. The winning president was expected to take the trophy back to his office and leave it on his desk for the entire month. The presence of the "Golden Egg" raised questions from visitors and led to telling the visitor how he got the award. It also gave the president a chance to be a model for treating mistakes as opportunities to learn how to do it better, rather than as situations requiring blame. It legitimized the importance of learning from our failures, rather than using them to punish, and promoted the increase in trust, openness, and creativity.

D. Taboos

Taboos are behaviors contrary to the values we seek to affirm, i.e., things that need to be eliminated from the culture. In a culture of innovation, it is taboo to act negatively when a colleague suggests an idea, even if the idea appears to be outlandish. It's more productive to view the idea as a provocation that might lead to other ideas of value.

Another taboo is punishing employees for taking a risk that doesn't pan out. It is more productive to learn from mistakes than to punish.

Payoff of the Innovative Culture Program

The proof of the pudding is in the eating.

The Oxford Dictionary of Quotations dates this proverb back to the early 14th century. It relates to not knowing the outcome of an event until it actually occurs.

Over time, the program to create an innovative culture in the DuPont Industrial Products Division led to many visible bottom-line successes. Many examples were described earlier in this book, particularly in Chapter 5, Innovative Thinking Techniques. Three additional examples that stand out as testimony to the proof is in the pudding are described below.

Emergence of Innovator Champions

This example relates to emergence of a passionate innovator champion who applied his learning in a problem solving session that resulted in an annual savings of $6 million.

Jean Prideaux, a mechanical engineering Ph.D. and technical group manager, had no previous knowledge of the creativity and innovation field. One of the innovative thinking tools he had learned in an off-site workshop was "stretch thinking." He applied this technique in a group meeting designed to set annual objectives for improving manufactured polymer uniformity, crucial in spinning a high-quality Kevlar fiber. The previous annual goal of 5 percent improvement was difficult to achieve. Prideaux suggested that the goal be a 50 percent improvement!

The group was stunned, feeling that this would be an impossible task. He asked why. The response was: To do that, we would have to do this…This type of "stretch thinking" set in motion a program that, as Prideaux put it, failed miserably. The group achieved only 40 percent improvement. The following year they achieved another 25 percent on top of that. The savings from this accomplishment was $6 million annually. This example of the value of innovative thinking motivated others across the site to learn and apply innovative thinking techniques in their programs.

Environmental Respect Award

This example involves a Kevlar technical/manufacturing team that won a corporate Environmental Respect award that the manufacturing manager credited to the innovative thinking program.

The DuPont Company established in 1990 a Chairman's Environmental Respect Award that was sought after by hundreds of DuPont divisions. The award was won by a joint effort of a Kevlar technical/manufacturing team by reducing process waste in the polymer area by more than 80 percent, saving the business $3 million annually. The manufacturing manager wrote:

> Many of the efforts undertaken by Kevlar team members were considered or attempted in the past without success. One of the reasons they succeeded this time is that Kevlar has had a program to change the environment for creativity and innovation and give to the organization the skills necessary to do their job more creatively.

Patent Trends

One of the benefits of an innovative culture is that it inspires inventiveness. During the period that innovative culture was enhanced in the Industrial Products Division, the number of filed patents soared. In the 3-year period following initiation of the effort, notices of inventions by R&D people surged from 40 in 1987 to 148 in 1989. In the same period, patent filings climbed from 16 to 67. Patent allowances nearly tripled from 10 to 28 and were on the rise.

Measurement of Innovative Culture

What gets measured, gets done.

Measuring progress in any endeavor provides incentives to get it done better. If it is measured, people pay attention to it.

Health care organizations that undertake a program to enhance innovative culture would benefit by measuring progress in the program. Two surveys that help to measure progress are described below.

Innovative Culture Survey

I designed an Innovative Culture Survey that provides information on employees' views of the environment for innovative thinking and innovation. It's a way to track progress toward the vision of an innovative culture using a questionnaire that contains 16 specific questions and two general ones that are posed to members of the organization. The questionnaire provides feedback relative to the four components of the culture change model—status, rituals, totems, taboos—described earlier in this chapter. The survey is included in Appendix 1.

The survey not only measures—the proof of the pudding is in the eating—but also serves as a platform for communication between front-line workers and the management. The results give management information about what improvements might be needed to motivate people to think more innovatively, suggest new ideas, and work hard at bringing best ideas to reality. For example, if a survey indicates that some people are dissatisfied with credit they deserve for contributions made in team projects, steps would be taken to remedy the situation.

Innovation Trends Survey

I designed this survey to track progress in the flow of innovator-driven bottom-line innovations. It consists of a five-step process that a management team might follow to periodically measure rate and amount of innovation in all sectors of the organization. When publicized, it enables innovators to share knowledge gained about success factors, potential pitfalls, and best practices. It raises awareness that innovations are valued by management and are expected. It also recognizes people and teams for their valuable contributions. The survey process is described in Appendix 2.

Corporate Environment

Corporate management in the DuPont Company is highly supportive of an environment for creative thinking and innovation. The Center for Creativity and Innovation, established in 1989, was dedicated to helping employees learn and apply creative thinking techniques of value in problem solving and opportunity searching. The formation and operation of the center during the period in which I was involved is described in Reference 1.

This section describes two needs-driven innovations accomplished because of a supportive environment.

1. Crawfish Bait Innovation Story

A "permitting" environment aids innovative thinking in needs-driven innovation. This is illustrated in the Crawfish Bait Innovation story. This story also highlights several success-oriented innovator characteristics and key steps in the innovation process, starting out with recognition of a need.

The focus of this innovation is crawfish, which for hundreds of years were a primary food source for people of French-Canadian heritage living in the bayous of Louisiana. Many continued to live close to the water, where fishing and trapping were a way of life and provided income. In recent years, the popularity of crawfish and the Cajun way of cooking had spread nationwide. Cajun restaurants had sprung up in many locations. Patrons enjoyed the flavor of the culture as much as the flavor of the food. All of that had led to a huge demand for crawfish.

The Need

Jay Daigle was a production worker in a DuPont plant but raised crawfish on the side. This part-time business was meant to be a relatively effortless source of additional income. But there was a problem—none of the available crawfish bait lasted long enough to make setting the traps worthwhile. Artificial baits could be used in the summertime, but they lasted for only a few hours. In the wintertime, the only bait was fish, but it was hard to handle and had many disadvantages. There was clearly a need for long-lasting crawfish bait.

The Idea

Daigle had an idea that an inert polymer matrix might make the bait last longer. He took his idea to his friend, Mal Smith, a chemist. They formed a team and began bootlegging some experiments. They tested the samples at Daigle's crawfish farm. The results were encouraging so they continued their pursuit of improved bait. Because the polymer was not water soluble, they could provide farmers with bait that would disappear only when the crawfish ate it. This increased bait life dramatically, from several hours up to as many as 7 days. They talked with farmers, who were enthusiastic about the concept. Everyone wanted it and there was a market need for something they could provide.

The "Permitting" Environment

At first, the project was kept under wraps. Smith and Daigle borrowed time from other projects to develop their long-lasting crawfish bait. There was an odor in the back of the laboratory, but everybody looked the other way. Their supervisors must have known that they were doing something outside of their assigned jobs but never asked.

The innovators finally told people about their project. At first, people said it wouldn't work. The plant manager said they had invented the wrong thing. But when they explained their concept and its advantages, people offered to help and volunteered to join the team.

The team's basic philosophy was that, if they had a good product, they ought to get it to the marketplace quickly. They felt it would be better to refine the product in the marketplace rather than in the laboratory. They believed that the reason many products don't reach the marketplace sooner is because they are "tested to death."

"Warrioring" for Their Idea

Smith and Daigle went to the DuPont Agricultural Products Department, but they were turned down because crawfish bait didn't fit into its product line. Still, they were persistent about moving ahead. It was up to the innovators to find their own way to market.

The team decided that the best approach was to make some bait and give it away to farmers to try in their traps and compare with other products. The trials were a success. The farmers wanted the bait and wanted it badly. This demand created suction in the marketplace. The farmers called on the Agricultural Products marketing people requesting information about availability. Now the Ag Products people called for help in producing and selling the crawfish bait.

Bottom-Line Success

The giveaway was a huge success, and farmers came back for more. Crawfish bait was just the beginning. It was commercialized by DuPont as Aquabind® and sold in other markets such as binder and shrimp feeds. The technology and rights were purchased from DuPont by the two innovators who formed their own company. Applications for the technology were expanded.

Learnings

The crawfish bait innovation is an example of an innovator having an awareness of a market need that could not be filled by competitive products. He generated a creative idea to meet that need and formed a team with another person who had the expertise necessary to explore and demonstrate the idea. A "permitting" environment enabled the team to bootleg the project. It was kept quiet until the team had confidence that the idea would work and that there was a market for the product. They refined the product in the field rather than in the laboratory.

The innovators were persistent. They did not give up, even though the project had been turned down because it didn't fit into the established business. They "warriored" for their idea to keep it alive. In this case, they created suction for the new product by taking it to the marketplace and sampling potential customers. In the process, they leveraged the company image to add credibility to the development. Finally, the concept started small but bloomed into a potentially large opportunity.

2. "Are We Creative Yet?" Innovation Story[37, 38]

Humor, or lack of it, can be an important source of new concepts that ignite new innovations. Humor was the driving force for publication of an innovative cartoon book entitled *Are We Creative Yet?* This book pairs humorous cartoons with basic concepts in creative thinking and innovation.

The Need

The story began in 1987 when an ad hoc group of DuPont employees formed an OZ Creative Thinking Network with the objective of broadly disseminating concepts in creativity and innovation across the company. In the early stages of this network, monthly hour-long luncheon meetings were held to share thoughts and knowledge about creativity and innovation. The OZ name was coined during one of these luncheons when we considered ourselves a "creativity pick-up team on a bumpy road to a brighter future as in the *Wizard of OZ*." The OZ name stuck.

At one of these luncheons, Fred Dickson, an innovative patent associate, came for the first time and shared his thinking about the need to understand how creative people think and how others can be taught this important skill. He felt that:

> Most books on creativity and innovation were too vague, too lofty, and not much fun.

The Idea

Dickson noticed that many Frank and Ernest cartoons by Bob Thaves had a creativity theme. He wondered whether this could be used to add humor to a serious message and suggested that this might be accomplished by a cartoon book. This idea was reinforced by a phrase in the OZ Group's aim statement:

> …to enable a culture for creative thinking and innovation in a way which is…fun rather than drudgery.

The group decided the idea was worth implementing.

Implementation

The first step was for Dickson to travel to California to gain buy-in, permission, and the help of Bob Thaves. Having done this, the next step was for an OZ team to screen 6,000 Frank and Ernest Cartoons, from which 150 were selected as being pertinent.

A company-wide contest was held, with management support, soliciting short essays from employees expressing their views and experiences in the field of creativity and innovation that best fit the cartoons. The contest was publicized in the DuPont Directions magazine. Kits of the 150 cartoons were provided to entrants. Winners' names would appear in the book.

This cartoon/essay pair was published as an example:

Reprinted with permission. Frank and Ernest Cartoons ©Thaves.

The team approach to problem solving and communication will often lead to a simple solution to what at first may appear to be a complicated problem. Each member, including customer and supplier, is like the piece of a puzzle working with other pieces to better understand the situation. What looked like a 'mess' can then become a success.

More than 400 essay/cartoon pairs were received from employees in over 25 states and 10 countries. The perceived 60 best, paired with 105 cartoons, were selected for publication. Pricing advice was obtained from the corporate marketing committee. In-house printing and distribution were aided by a marketing communications OZ Group member. Legal agreements with the cartoon publisher were handled by an attorney who was an OZ Group member.

The cartoon book cover is shown below.

Examples of cartoon/essay pairs received from across the company:

Reprinted with permission. Frank and Ernest Cartoons ©Thaves.

Successful problem-solvers know that what's important is to get the problem solved, not necessarily to get it solved solo. When you've come to a mental dead-end and need a better roadmap, leave your ego at a rest stop and ask others to help in navigating. Organize a team creativity session based on brainstorming, synectics, or other techniques. It's fun and mentally challenging, You'll be riding in the passing lane in no time.

Reprinted with permission. Frank and Ernest Cartoons © Thaves.

The last thing a leader of innovative people wants is to be followed by a herd. That leader should expect and demand "mavericks," "troublemakers," "bureaucracy busters." He needs people who will constructively change the direction in which a company is headed and the standard ways of doing things.

Commercialization

The cartoon book idea took 3 years to bring to market and was introduced in May 1990 with the following forward by DuPont Chairman Ed Woolard:

"There is plenty of room throughout DuPont for "heroes" in all types of jobs. We intend to provide hero status to those who show us how to GET products to the marketplace more promptly and more creatively.

The OZ Group's Are We Creative Yet? cartoon book illustrates the creativity of our people and describes in a humorous vein some of the basic concepts in creativity and innovation."

By 1992, more than 20,000 copies were either sold internally or donated to educational and nonprofit groups, such as the American Creativity Association. The decision to sell the books rather than to distribute them to all 140,000 DuPont employees was made on the premise that people value something more when they pay for it. The funds were used to cover expenses for speakers at OZ Group meetings.

Health Care Innovations

The approach to establish an innovative culture in an organization, described earlier in this chapter, may be of value to hospital innovators striving to establish a hospital safety culture. The three innovations described below, and the one described in the previous chapter, deal with this needs-driven issue in hospitals.

Promoting a Culture for Hospital Safety[39]

Summary of the Program

Northwestern Memorial Hospital holds monthly patient safety meetings, known as Patient Safety Morbidity and Mortality Conferences, that serve as a forum for clinicians and staff from all levels and multiple disciplines to hear about and discuss adverse events that have occurred at the hospital. Led by a moderator and staff panel, the meetings provide an opportunity for participants to not only hear case presentations but also to actively evaluate the root causes of adverse events and suggest work redesign steps geared toward preventing the recurrence of similar events in the future. Staff responsible for the processes involved in the event attend the conference, incorporate these ideas into their improvement work, and are accountable for reporting on implementation. Based on the success of these meetings, additional monthly meetings have been added that focus on nursing-specific and pharmacy-specific safety issues. The program significantly improved staff perceptions of the organization's safety culture and increased the reporting of adverse events.

Although many health care organizations attempt to create a culture of safety, most clinicians and staff continue to fear a punitive response when adverse events occur. The innovative hospital leadership recognized the need to design initiatives that would promote open dialogue about adverse events. This would help the organization to develop a culture of safety.

The Needs-Driven Innovation

To meet the need, the hospital leadership charged a dedicated group of nurses and pharmacists to focus on the safety issue. This led to creating a user-friendly electronic adverse event reporting system; implementing a number of collaborative, interdisciplinary quality improvement projects; and administering an AHRQ Hospital Survey on Patient Safety Culture.

After a guest speaker held a case-specific discussion with hospital leaders on patient safety, these leaders decided that engaging clinicians and staff in the discussion of specific cases could enhance the organization's patient safety culture and lead to care process improvements. Subsequently, the hospital's medical director for quality and patient safety initiated monthly conferences.

The monthly patient safety meetings, known as Patient Safety Morbidity and Mortality Conferences, serve as a forum for clinicians and staff from all levels and multiple disciplines to hear about and discuss adverse events that have occurred at the hospital. Led by a moderator and staff panel, the meetings provide an opportunity for participants to not only hear case presentations but also to actively evaluate the root causes of adverse events and suggest work redesign steps geared toward preventing the recurrence of similar events in the future. Staff responsible for the processes involved in the event attend the conference, incorporate these ideas into their improvement work, and are accountable for reporting on implementation.

Results

Based on the success of these meetings, additional monthly meetings have been added that focus on nursing-specific and pharmacy-specific safety issues. The program significantly improved staff perceptions of the organization's safety culture and increased the reporting of adverse events.

Nurse Knowledge Exchange[40]

Several organizations are repeat innovators and clearly have a culture of innovation through various processes. An example is Kaiser Permanente. This company is the source of several dozen innovation profiles reported in the AHRQ Health Care Innovations Exchange web site. The following is one of them.

Summary of the Program

Nurse Knowledge Exchange is a four-step process related to nurse shift changes that is designed to enhance patient safety by conveying vital patient information accurately, concisely, and consistently. Handoff of each patient from one nurse to the next occurs at the patient's bedside and includes patient participation. Nurse Knowledge Exchange optimizes the time spent transferring patient care from one nursing shift to the next, leading to high levels of patient and nurse satisfaction. Although no hard data are available, the program is likely to lead to improved patient safety. The Institute for Healthcare Improvement has identified Nurse Knowledge Exchange as one of the best practices for handoff procedures to improve patient outcomes.

The Need

Kaiser Permanente, a large, nonprofit, national health care organization headquartered in Oakland, CA, comprises health plans, medical groups, medical centers, and their subsidiaries. A headquarters-based Kaiser Permanente Innovation Consultancy partnered with IDEO, experts in innovation methodology, to work with leaders in Kaiser Permanente's four hospital regions to identify opportunities for innovation within their hospitals. Nurse communication, especially at shift change, was unanimously identified as a process in need of significant improvement.

The Needs-Driven Innovation

Four sites were selected to develop, implement, and pilot test a program designed to improve the nurse shift-change process. Nurse Knowledge Exchange is a four-step process related to nurse shift changes that is designed to enhance patient safety by conveying vital patient information accurately, concisely, and consistently. Handoff of each patient from one nurse to the next occurs at the patient's bedside and includes patient participation. Nurse Knowledge Exchange optimizes the time spent transferring patient care from one nursing shift to the next, leading to high levels of patient and nurse satisfaction. Although no hard data are available, the program is likely to lead to improved patient safety.

The Institute for Healthcare Improvement has identified Nurse Knowledge Exchange as one of the best practices for handoff procedures to improve patient outcomes.

Results

Pre- and post-implementation comparisons made during a pilot study of the program show that Nurse Knowledge Exchange has optimized the time spent transferring patient care from one nursing shift to the next; post-implementation surveys indicate that the program has led to high levels of patient and nurse satisfaction.

Use by Other Organizations

The Nurse Knowledge Exchange innovation has now been implemented in 33 Kaiser Permanente hospitals.

Reduced Hospital-Acquired Infections[41]

Summary of the Program

The Billings Clinic, a not-for-profit organization in Billings, MT, addressed its rising rate of methicillin-resistant Staphylococcus aureus (MRSA) infections by making infection control a top, culture-oriented institutional priority. It created a comprehensive package that combines adoption and monitoring of strict infection control protocols, active surveillance, training and education, and the solicitation and implementation of employee ideas through an approach known as "positive deviance." According to information provided in June 2009, after the implementation of the program, the incidence of health care-associated MRSA infections decreased by 81 percent from the end of 2005 through the end of 2008. The reduction in health care-associated MRSA infections from 2005 through 2008 has continued through March 31, 2010.

The Need

MRSA infections are an increasingly common, serious, expensive problem that can often be prevented if evidence-based infection control procedures are followed. This is an increasingly common problem with serious human and financial costs. In 2005, an estimated 94,360 individuals developed serious MRSA infections in U.S. hospitals, and roughly 18,650 hospitalized patients died of causes related to serious MRSA infections. In 2004, MRSA accounted for 63 percent of staph infections, up from 2 percent in 1974 and 22 percent in 1995. The average hospital MRSA infection costs $20,000 to treat. Despite using an evidence-based approach for preventing MRSA transmission, the Billings Clinic in Montana has experienced a steady rise in MRSA rates in recent years; between 2000 and 2005, the number of hospital-associated MRSA infections per 1,000 patient days rose from 0.15 to 0.81. The main method by which the infection is transmitted is through human hands, especially health care workers' hands. Hands may become contaminated with MRSA bacteria by contact with infected or colonized patients. Established MRSA infection control protocols have been shown to be effective in preventing MRSA transmission, but hospital staff members often fail to follow these protocols. A vital need was to establish a culture for procedures necessary to reduce MRSA infections.

The Needs-Based Innovation

The Billings Clinic has transformed its organizational culture into one in which MRSA prevention behaviors are a top priority. This transformation has been accomplished through use of established infection control protocols, active surveillance, training and education/feed-back, and the solicitation and implementation of ideas from frontline employees through an approach known as "positive deviance." Key elements of the program include creating a culture where MRSA control is a top priority, with a focus on supporting employee-generated ideas. Billings leaders have adopted and promoted the positive deviance approach to create social and behavioral change, as positive deviance emphasizes the role of front-line employees in generating solutions to problems.

These leaders realize that, to encourage employees to come forward with solutions, they need to create a culture in which employees are motivated to do so. In communications to employees, Billings leaders emphasize the significance of the MRSA issue and the need for employees to think of infection control as their problem rather than something handled only by infection control specialists. To that end, they encourage employees to share their ideas on infection control and to point out and correct any errors they may witness in the infection control behaviors of coworkers.

Staff members are required to wash hands before and after every patient contact and to disinfect all items that come in contact with MRSA-positive patients. A number of employee-generated ideas have increased adherence to this protocol. For example, staff began disinfecting previously overlooked items that can spread MRSA, such as keys to drug storage compartments and dinner trays. To accommodate the increased use of disposable gowns, gloves, and other items that help prevent transmission,

Billings Clinic purchased larger garbage cans that help reduce the time spent emptying trash. Isolation carts were purchased so that isolation precaution supplies were organized and readily available for staff outside patient rooms.

Physicians decided to begin rounding on MRSA patients at the end of the day, when they had more time to take precautions. In addition, some male physicians stopped wearing ties because of their potential to transmit MRSA.

Every intensive care unit (ICU) patient receives a nasal swab test for MRSA on admission, transfer, or discharge. The ICU patients who stay longer than 1 week are swabbed every 7 days. Billings Clinic also switched to a different culture medium, which reduces the time it takes to get results, allowing staff to begin taking contact precautions with MRSA-positive patients more quickly.

Billings Clinic created an alert system that flags all patients with a history of MRSA and electronically sends a notice to the units with an order to begin isolation precautions. The purpose of the flagging system is to begin isolation more quickly, thereby reducing the potential for MRSA transmission. Patients infected or colonized with MRSA are placed on contact isolation protocols based on the Centers for Disease Control and Prevention (CDC) 2006 Multi-Drug Organism Resistant Guidelines.

Hospital administrators distribute quarterly data on MRSA infection rates to all hospital employees. Staff members in some units, such as the ICU, receive this information each week.

Billings has put in place a variety of educational and training programs focused on reducing MRSA transmission. Each unit holds a monthly meeting in which they discuss MRSA prevention practices. The group's coordinators use a range of educational methods during these sessions, including imitation, where an experienced worker demonstrates a tactic (e.g., the proper technique for nasal swabbing or disinfecting a room) and then participants practice the tactic with each other.

In response to front-line worker requests for more training, program coordinators converted an unused space into a simulated patient room. This space serves as host to a mandatory 1.5-hour training session in which 12 to 15 individuals participate in one of four improvisational sketches. After each MRSA-related scenario is acted out, the audience provides feedback about what the staff did well and where they can improve. This scenario-playing emphasizes a key positive deviance principle—that participants find it easier to act their way into a new way of thinking than to think their way into a new way of acting.

Results

Pre- and post-implementation comparisons suggest that this comprehensive program has significantly reduced the incidence of hospital-acquired MRSA infections, due primarily to better adherence to infection control procedures such as regular surveillance. Since beginning this cultural change initiative, Billings Clinic experienced 81 percent fewer health care-associated MRSA infections, which resulted in more than $1.1 million in avoided costs, according to information provided in June 2009.

Innovative Culture Survey

This survey has 16 specific and 2 general questions. It can be provided to individuals in an organization with the objective of gauging the environment for innovative thinking and innovation. It helps to measure progress in a program designed to promote an innovative culture.

Survey

Please indicate the number corresponding to your perception of your working environment where, on a scale of 1 to 5, 1 is "too little" and 5 is "to a great extent."

In my organization the leadership *encourages:*   Number

1. Freedom for people to express new and contro-
    versial ideas that are welcomed and evaluated.

2. Training of employees in the tools of creative
    thinking and their practical application in yield-
    ing valuable innovations.

3. Challenging assignments which best fit people's
    thinking styles where some are best at generat-
    ing ideas and others at taking ideas to reality.

4. Innovation in all segments of the organization
    including R&D, Marketing, Manufacturing, and
    Business functions.

In my organization there are *repetitive interactions:* Number

5. Individuals and teams routinely apply creative thinking tools in problem solving and opportunity-searching for new innovations. ☐

6. Events are scheduled periodically with a creativity and innovation theme that continually energizes the organization to participate in the program. ☐

7. People voluntarily attend creativity and innovation seminars and workshops scheduled periodically to help expand their knowledge in the field. ☐

8. Schedules of creativity and innovation seminars and workshops are periodically communicated to a network of interested employees. ☐

In my organization there are these *emblems of success:* Number

9. People are recognized and rewarded for successfully applying new ideas to solve problems in their assigned program. ☐

10. People are rewarded for suggesting creative ideas with business value outside their assigned program that are successfully implemented. ☐

11. Stories of innovation successes are widely publicized through presentation at special events, email, and occasionally by videos. ☐

12. Champions at all levels in the organization who use creativity and innovation tools are rewarded for setting the example for others. ☐

In my organization there are these *deterrents* to creativity and innovation:

13. Risk taking is discouraged rather than encouraged, and punished if unsuccessful, rather than learning from failures and mistakes. ☐

14. There is too little resource support to help solve problems creatively. ☐

15. People have little time to think creatively about new innovative business opportunities or finding new and better ways of doing things. ☐

16. New ideas are ignored or discouraged. ☐

General — List on back of page:

The two to three most important factors in your working environment supporting creative thinking and innovation.

The two to three most important factors in your working environment inhibiting creative thinking and innovation.

Appendix 2

Innovation Trends Survey

The Innovation Trends Survey is a five-step process aimed at annually tracking the number and practical value of successful innovations generated from all units within the organization. The survey provides management with a measurement of progress, publicizes successes, shares knowledge about creative thinking and innovation, and gives recognition to individuals and teams. The process is as follows:

1. The company President or CEO requests Directors of the R&D, Marketing, Manufacturing, and Business functions to identify and explain all innovations that have been accomplished in their organization in the past 1-2 years.

2. Each Director identifies successful innovations in his or her organization in the area of new products, new processes, human resources, work practices, cost reduction, finance, information systems, environmental protection, quality, etc.

3. Individuals and teams involved in each innovation are requested to submit an abstract describing the innovation with these guidelines:
    - Describe the business need, the creative idea, the process of taking idea to reality, and financial or other benefits.

- Tell the innovation "story" in a way that highlights success factors such as creative thinking, sponsorship, supportive environment, risk taking, overcoming barriers, and speed of delivery.

4. The innovation abstracts are communicated companywide through email and/or written reports. This enables innovators and teams to share their learning and enthusiasm for the innovation process with other innovators and potential new ones.

5. In some cases an organization might sponsor an event where innovators and teams present the innovation "story." This could be accompanied by award presentations if deemed appropriate by the management.

The Innovation Survey is conducted annually to measure progress and maintain momentum in the program to build a more creative, innovative company.

References

1. David Tanner, *Total Creativity in Business & Industry: Road Map to Building a More Innovative Organization* (Des Moines, IA, Advanced Practical Thinking Training, Inc., 1997), (Tokyo, Japan, The Nikkan Kogyo Shimbun, Ltd., 1998)

2. David Tanner, *Igniting Innovation Through the Power of Creative Thinking* (West Des Moines, IA, Myers House LLC, 2008)

3. Peter F. Drucker, *Innovation and Entrepreneurship Practices & Principles,* (Harper & Row Publishers, Inc. 1985)

4. Alex F. Osborn, *Applied Imagination: Principles and Procedures of Creative Problem solving,* (New York: Charles Scribner's Sons, 1953)

5. Edward de Bono, *Mechanism of Mind,* (Penguin Books, 1976)

6. Edward de Bono, *Serious Creativity,* (Harper Business, 1992)

7. Edward de Bono, *Six Thinking Hats,* (Back Bay Books, 1999)

8. Ned Herrmann, *The Creative Brain,* (Ned Herrmann Group, 1988)

9. Ned Herrmann, *The Whole Brain® Business Book* (McGraw-Hill, Harvard Business School, 1996)

10. Michael J. Kirton, *Adapters and Innovators: Styles of Creativity and Problem Solving,* (London & Routledge, 1994)

11. AHRQ Health Care Innovations Exchange Web Site, http://www.innovations.ahrq.gov/content.aspx?id=1690, Original publication, April 18, 2008; Last updated December 22, 2010

12. AHRQ Health Care Innovations Exchange web site www.innovations.ahrq.gov/content.aspx?id=95, Original publication April 14, 2008; Last updated November 24, 2010

13. AHRQ Health Care Innovations Exchange Web Site, www.innovations.ahrq.gov/content.aspx?id=1742, Original publication April 14, 2008; Last updated March 3, 2010

14. David Tanner, Jim Fitzgerald, and Brian Phillips, *Kevlar–From Laboratory to Marketplace Through Innovation,* the DuPont Company Advanced Materials International Conference, Wilmington, DE, November, 1988

15. David Tanner, Jim Fitzgerald, and Brian Phillips, *The Kevlar Story–An Advanced Materials Case History,* (Angev. Chem., Adv. Mater:, Nr. 5, 1989)

16. AHRQ Health Care Innovations Exchange Web Site, www.innovations.ahrq.gov/content.aspx?id=1787, Original publication August 18, 2008; Last updated October 7, 2009

17. AHRQ Health Care Innovations Exchange Web Site, www.innovations.ahrq.gov/content.aspx?id=2051, Original publication August 18, 2008; Last updated July 7, 2010

18. AHRQ Health Care Innovations Exchange Web Site, www.innovations.ahrq.gov/content.aspx?id=2201, *Real Time Surgery Tracking,* Original publication September, 15, 2008; Last updated October 13, 2010

19. Stan Gryskiewicz, *Creativity in Organizations: A Jazz Musician's Perspective,* (Center for Creative Leadership, Greensboro, NC, 1988)

20. Charles Prather, *The Manager's Guide to Fostering Innovation and Creativity in Teams,* (The McGraw-Hill Companies, 2009)

21. AHRQ Health Care Innovations Exchange Web Site, www.innovations.ahrq.gov/content.aspx?id=1809, Original publication April 14, 2008; Last updated April 28, 2010

22. AHRQ Health Care Innovations Exchange Web Site, www.innovations.ahrq.gov/content.aspx?id=1688, Original publication August 4, 2008; Last updated January 26, 2011

23. AHRQ Health Care Innovations Exchange Web Site, www.innovations.ahrq.gov/content.aspx?id=2826, Original publication, August 4, 2010; Last updated November 3, 2010

24. Edward Glassman, *Creativity Handbook: Shift Paradigms and Harvest Creative Thinking at Work*, (Chapel Hill, NC: The LCS Press, 1991)

25. Edward de Bono, *The Use of Lateral Thinking*, (Toronto: Penguin Books, 1976)

26. Edward de Bono, *Lateral Thinking for Management*, Penguin Books Ltd., 1990)

27. *Edward de Bono's Thinking Course*, (New York: Facts on File, 1994)

28. de Bono Thinking Systems,® www.debonothinkingsystems.com

29. Roger von Oech, *A Whack on the Side of the Head: How to Unlock Your Mind for Innovation*, (New York: Harper & Row, 1988)

30. Alan G. Robinson & Sam Stern, *Corporate Creativity— How Innovation and Improvement Actually Happen*, (San Francisco, CA, Berrett-Koehler Publishers, Inc., 1988)

31. AHRQ Health Care Innovations Exchange Web Site, www.innovations.ahrq.gov/content.aspx?id=2113, Original publication, October 27; Last updated July 21, 2010

32. AHRQ Health Care Innovations Exchange Web Site, www.innovations.ahrq.gov/content.aspx?id=1772, Original publication April 14, 2010; Last updated May 12, 2010

33. AHRQ Health Care Innovations Exchange Web Site, www.innovations.ahrq.gov/content.aspx?id=2646, Original publication January 27, 2010; Last updated March 11, 2011

34. AHRQ Health Care Innovations Exchange Web Site, www.innovations.ahrq.gov/content.aspx?id=2699, Original publication April 14, 2010

35. AHRQ Health Care Innovations Exchange Web Site, www.innovations.ahrq.gov/content.aspx?id=1719, Original publication April 18, 2008; Last updated March 11, 2011

36. AHRQ Health Care Innovations Exchange Web Site, www.innovations.ahrq.gov/content.aspx?id=2841, Original publication October 13, 2010

37. The *Are We Creative Yet?* cartoon book (DuPont company publication, 1990)

38. The *Are We Creative Yet?* cartoon book second edition (American Creativity Association ACA Press, Austin, TX, 2005)

39. AHRQ Health Care Innovations Exchange Web Site, www.innovations.ahrq.gov/content.aspx?id=2772, Original publication June 23, 2010

40. AHRQ Health Care Innovations Exchange Web Site, www.innovations.ahrq.gov/content.aspx?id=1803, Original publication April 28, 2008; Last updated February 2, 2011

41. AHRQ Health Care Innovations Exchange Web Site, www.innovations.ahrq.gov/content.aspx?id=1774, Original publication December 18, 2008; Last updated September 29, 2010

Index

P

Palo Alto Community Breast Health Project, 13, 14

Patent trends, 128

Patient safety, 139-142

Pioneering Research Laboratory, 26

Positive Thinking, 21, 22, 27, 29, 71, 74

Prather, Charles, 43

Prideaux, Jean, 123, 127

Primary care, 86, 87

Principles of Effective Thinking (POET) workshop, 121, 123

Problem solving session/process, 8, 22, 37-41, 45, 57, 59, 72, 106, 107, 109, 121, 123, 124, 127

Problem solving Walk-Around™, 65, 66

Pronovost, Peter, 109, 110

Proverb, 3, 6, 21, 23, 24, 126

Provocations (random word, escape, stepping stone), 54-58, 60, 61, 126

Prudential Life Insurance, 72

R

Ragsdale, Floyd, 67

Regional Medical Center, 35, 36

Resourcing a task force, 104, 105

Rituals, 120, 121, 123, 129

Role of the Innovator, 2, 19, 31

S

Safety culture, 109-111, 139, 140

Salk, Jonas, 61

San Mateo Medical Center, 11, 12

Seton Northwest Hospital, 88, 89, 91

Shields, Steve, 2, 33-35

Six Thinking Hats, 9, 41, 72, 73, 75-82, 103, 123

Smith, Mal, 131, 132

Sources of innovation, 2, 5, 6

Spunbonded Nonwoven fabrics, 70

Status, 2, 21, 22, 25, 26, 31, 34-36, 69, 90, 120, 121, 129, 137

Stein, Morris, 70

Storytelling, 83, 85

Structuring a team, 104

Surgery, 35

Survey

    Innovation trends, 130, 151

    Innovative culture, 129, 147

T

Taboos, 120, 126, 129

Teflon®, 5, 78, 124

Texas A&M University, 70

Thaves, Bob, 134

Totems, 120, 125, 129

Tyvek®, 69, 78, 100, 117, 124

U

University of California San Francisco, 12-14, 51

V

Veterans Health System, 46, 47

von Oech, Roger, 68

W

Washington Post, 118

Whole Brain® Thinking, 9, 53, 64, 66, 95, 97-100

Williams, Robin, 52

Woolard, Ed, 137

WrapAround Milwaukee, 112, 113

Published by

Rockville Institute
1600 Research Boulevard
Rockville, MD 20850-3129
www.rockvilleinstitute.org

31489.0912.112141

Made in the USA
Columbia, SC
09 May 2018